D1015825

EFFICIENCY IN DEATH:

The Manufacturers of
Anti-Personnel Weapons

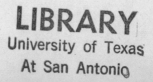

EFFICIENCY
IN DEATH:

The Manufacturers of
Anti-Personnel Weapons

The Council on
Economic Priorities

PERENNIAL LIBRARY
Harper & Row, Publishers
New York and Evanston

EFFICIENCY IN DEATH: THE MANUFACTURERS OF
ANTI-PERSONNEL WEAPONS

Copyright © 1970 by The Council on Economic Priorities

This book, in a slightly different form, comprised the first in-depth study produced by The Council on Economic Priorities. Part of the study was encapsulated in the *Economic Priorities Report*, Vol. 1, No. 1, a journal available from The Council on Economic Priorities, 1028 Connecticut Avenue, N.W., Washington, D.C., 20036.

First PERENNIAL LIBRARY edition published 1970

Library of Congress Catalog Card Number: 78–130450

Contents

We would like to acknowledge the aid of NARMIC (National Action/Research on the Military Industrial Complex, a project of the American Friends Service Committee in Philadelphia) in the creation of this book. Their publication, *Weapons For Counter-Insurgency,* use of their research library, and their suggestions greatly aided us in our work.

Foreword

The Council on Economic Priorities is an information and research center that publishes unbiased data on corporate policies, practices, and products as they affect society.

The Council recognizes that corporate decisions have a vital and immediate impact on the quality of our lives. It believes that every American should know how different corporations meet human needs:

Would you like to know how effectively companies control pollution?

Would you like to know which firms have contracts with the Department of Defense?

Would you like to know which firms provide better economic equality for minorities?

Would you like to know the policies of firms that conduct business in the Union of South Africa or in Greece?

The Council on Economic Priorities publishes such information along with the brand names of these corporation's consumer products, the affiliations of their directors and chief executives, summary financial data, and plant locations. This information is available in our monthly journal, the *Economic Priorities Report*. The *Report* summarizes our In-Depth Studies, profiles on corporations, and reports on private and governmental campaigns for corporate responsibility. The last page of this book carries a subscription form for the *Report* and for upcoming studies. Our next study will examine pollution and the paper-pulping industry.

In preparation now for publication by Harper & Row in the Fall is a *Student Guide to Corporations*, a compendium of brief, factual information about the military production, employment practices, efforts to control pollution, and the conduct of business abroad of some 75 to 100 corporations.

Introduction

Over 100 U.S. corporations receive and execute government contracts in excess of $300 million a year for the research, development and production of anti-personnel weapons. These weapons are one kind of a whole series of conventional arms which are designed for limited warfare and which are being used extensively in Vietnam. Anti-personnel weapons have no effect against buildings or factories; they can do very little damage to military fortifications or vehicles; in fact, they cannot even harm military equipment, targets or personnel protected behind sandbags. They are aimed at only one target—people, and against this target their destructive force is very great. They can wound and kill effectively and are engineered to cover wide land areas in order to strike as large a number of people as possible.

Looking at the whole spectrum of war weapons production in this country, why have we chosen anti-personnel weapons and their manufacturers as the subject for this in-depth study? First of all, they were selected because they are one example of the conventional munition series. Analyzing the way in which they are developed and produced brings into focus the process by which all U.S. conventional arms production occurs.

Anti-personnel weapons were singled out of this conventional arms group because their effect on human life is perhaps the most brutal, and their use has significantly raised the toll of injury and death to the Vietnamese civilian population.

The International Conventions Relating to the Conduct of War (The Hague Conventions of 1907) drew distinctions between means of waging war that were acceptable and those that were not. Article 23 of the Conventions holds that:

> It is especially forbidden to employ arms, projectiles or materials calculated to cause unnecessary suffering.

The United States is a signatory to these Conventions. The term "unnecessary suffering" is, of course, open to a great deal of interpretation, but it should be kept in mind as we look closely at the nature and use of anti-personnel weapons.

We will then proceed to examine the U.S. corporations that participate in and profit from their production.

EFFICIENCY IN DEATH:

The Manufacturers of
Anti-Personnel Weapons

1. Kinds of
Anti-Personnel Weapons*

The general principle behind construction of anti-personnel weapons was explained by John S. Tompkins in his book, *The Weapons of World War III:*

> [Anti-personnel weapons represent] a growing family of munitions in which the killing power of conventional weapons has been made to approach that of small tactical nuclear weapons.

* NOTE: The information that is public knowledge on anti-personnel weapons is somewhat limited. Their usage has occasionally been reported in the daily press, and several articles on them have appeared in periodicals (these include: Don Duncan, "And Blessed Be the Fruit . . . ," *Ramparts,* May 1967; Eric Prokosch, "'Conventional' Killers," *The New Republic,* November 1, 1969; and occasional articles in *Aviation Week and Space Technology.* More technical information is contained in the Ordnance volume of the *DMS Market Intelligence Report* (a McGraw-Hill publication). Also, a recent pamphlet, *Weapons for Counter-Insurgency,* published by National Action/Research on the Military-Industrial Complex (NARMIC), a project of the American Friends Service Committee, describes anti-personnel weapons in one section.

[This] was done by substituting controlled fragments for the random pieces created by the explosion of a conventional bomb or shell. Most of the methods are highly classified, but the attempt to create predictable fragmentation patterns runs like a thread through present-day munitions design.[1]

The strong emphasis placed by the United States government on development and manufacture of these weapons in the past twenty years has been dictated by their effectiveness in limited war situations. As one officer pointed out:

Pilots [in Vietnam] prefer 2.75 inch rockets and fragmentation bombs [both anti-personnel weapons] as a rule rather than general purpose bombs. Most of the worthwhile targets are straw huts or targets in the open [i.e., people] and "frag" bombs and 2.75s are ideal for these targets.[2]

Fragmentation bombs and 2.75 rockets are the largest category of anti-personnel weapons now being used in Vietnam. The majority of fragmentation bombs belong to a group called cluster bomb units or CBUs. They are designed to be dropped from

1. John S. Tompkins, *The Weapons of World War III*, Doubleday, Garden City, New York, p. 116–117.
2. C. M. Plattner, "Marine Control of Air Tested in Combat," *Aviation Week and Space Technology*, Feb. 14, 1966, p. 90ff.

planes—either strategic bombers such as the Boeing B-52s or, more often, tactical fighter planes. CBUs consist of a large "mother bomb" which is expelled from the plane by compressed air—generally from an altitude of about 10,000-15,000 feet. An explosive charge blows open this mother bomb almost immediately, releasing its contents. In the very earliest and simplest CBUs, the mother bomb would release what are called "Lazy Dogs." These are:

> . . . non-explosive missiles a couple of inches long, solid iron and shaped like a tiny bomb. Falling by their own weight and the speed of the airplane they hit the ground with the force of a bullet. A CBU full of Lazy Dogs fills the air under it with a rain of projectiles that are both deadly and silent.[3]

The Lazy Dog pellets have a buckshot effect against people when they strike.

In more sophisticated and complex CBUs, the "mother bomb" releases objects that are in themselves little bombs. There are often as many as several hundred of these bomblets—each one about the size of a softball. They, in turn, explode and disperse hundreds of razor-sharp steel pellets. Cecil Brownlow, who has reported on the war in Vietnam in *Aviation Week and Space Technology*, has pointed out that while the standard bomblets contain these

---

3. Tompkins, *The Weapons of World War III*, p. 112.

pellets or fragments, other versions contain napalm or white phosphorus.[4]*

The bomblets travel through the air with a gliding and floating action which is explained in the *Yearbook of World Armaments and Disarmament, 1968/1969:*

> [They] are provided with small vanes around their outer surfaces. After the warhead opens, the effect of the vanes is to rotate the bomblets, giving them aerodynamic lift. The bomblets thus move sideways and their glide path during descent broadens, increasing their eventual coverage of the target area.[5]

Because of this action, these anti-personnel bomblets have been named "butterfly bombs." Their two most common varieties—both extensively used in Vietnam—are "Pineapples" and "Guavas." The pineapples explode on impact with the ground, spewing forth more than 200 steel pellets over a distance of about 10 meters. The pellets hit with the velocity of shot-

---

* NOTE: All of the cluster bombs are contained in dispensers. However, the dispensers have been developed for more general usage. More than one type of bomblet can be used in most dispensers. Also, they have been designed so that they can dispense incendiary, chemical and biological payloads.

4. Cecil Brownlow, "USAF Boosts North Viet ECM Jamming," *Aviation Week and Space Technology,* Feb. 2, 1967, p. 23.

5. The Stockholm International Peace Research Institute, *Yearbook of World Armaments and Disarmament, 1968/1969,* p. 117.

gun pellets fired from 3 or 4 yards. The effectiveness of pineapple bomblets, however, is diminished if the targets place themselves in bunkers. So, guava bomblets were developed to reduce the success of this tactic by the enemy. The guavas are equipped with proximity fuses and instead of exploding when they hit the ground, they explode about 30 feet in the air. They contain from 300 to 600 steel pellets which then shower down, spraying the ground and effectively penetrating bunkers.

Frank Harvey, a free-lance writer who has spent more than seventeen years reporting on the Air Force, was asked by one of its Public Information Officers in 1966 to come to Vietnam and report on the air war. The result was an article in *Flying* magazine and a book, *Air War: Vietnam.* In his book, Harvey calls anti-personnel weapons:

the deadliest weapons being used against people in Vietnam.

And he gives detailed descriptions of their striking power. Of guavas, he wrote:

. . . the little bomblets covered a wide swathe in a closely spaced pattern. They look like sparklers going off and were lethal to anybody within their range. Some types were fitted with delayed action fuses and went off later when people have come out thinking the area was safe. If a pilot used CBUs properly he could lawnmower for considerable distances, killing or maiming anybody on a path several hundred feet wide and many yards long.[6]

This delayed action fuse makes the weapon extremely effective psychologically as well as militarily. Enemy troops are not only afraid of the effects of being struck by fragments, but they are also subjected to an element of uncertainty as to when and where the bomblets will explode.

Guava bombs and components are made by General Tire and Rubber Company, City Investing Corporation, Tyler Corporation, Temco, Adventure Line Manufacturing Company, Ajax Hardware Manufacturing Company, Gibbs Die Casting Aluminum Corporation, Honeywell, National Lead Company, Superior Steel Ball Company, and Victor Comptometer Corporation.

The Vietnam war has spurred government efforts to develop increasingly effective anti-personnel weapons. In 1966, the Air Force awarded a $900,000 contract to Martin-Orlando to develop a version of the Bullpup B air-to-surface missile for fragmentation use against ground troops.[7] However, practical problems prevented its long-term use. Missiles cannot simply be dropped from planes like bombs. They must be guided to their target electronically by the planes. This necessitates flying at relatively low altitudes. In the early efforts to use this adaptation,

6. Frank Harvey, *Air War: Vietnam,* p. 57.
7. *Ordnance,* September–October, 1966, p. 144.

pilots were spending too much time directing the missiles to their targets and, consequently, became easy marks for anti-aircraft fire.

To replace the Bullpup, the Air Force decided to use "Sadeye'" cluster bombs which had been developed by the Navy.[8] "Sadeye" is a particular type of cluster bomb dispenser that is particularly well suited for low altitude bombing in the most modern high performance aircraft. "Sadeye" dispensers are manufactured by General Tire and Rubber Company (Aerojet General), City Investing Corporation (American Electric), Tyler Corporation, and Temco (Cullman Metalcraft).

Two more new types of cluster bombs have also been developed for use in Vietnam. Both are manufactured by Honeywell. The first is called the Tactical Fighter Dispenser Munition (TFDM) which, like "Sadeye," is intended for use in modern high performance tactical fighters. The TFDM's, however, utilize a new downward-ejection tube system for dispersing the cluster bombs. The second is called "Rockeye II"* and is perhaps the most advanced of the new cluster bomb systems. The "mother bomb"

---

* NOTE: Sadeye and Rockeye are two of a series of Navy conventional weapons called the "Eye Series". Others include: Bigeye, a chemical bomb; Briteye, a flare bomb; Deneye, an anti-material and anti-personnel weapon under development; Fireye, a fire bomb; Gladeye, a general purpose dispenser; Misteye, a flare bomb; Padeye, a bomblet dispenser under development; Snakeye, a bomb retarding device; and, finally, Walleye, a bomb that is guided by television.

8. DMS, in the "Dispensers, Bombs and Mines" section of the *Ordnance* volume.

contains 247 bomblets, each 2.1 inches long, and also contains a rocket motor. This motor ignites just after launching and spins the rocket. Simultaneously, a mechanical time fuse releases the bomblets. The spinning action serves to distribute the bomblets over a wide area. DMS reports in its *Ordnance* volume that the Navy and the Air Force are scheduling very heavy production for Rockeye II during Fiscal year 1970.

Another type of fragmentation bomb, widely used in Vietnam but not in cluster bomb form, is the 2.75 inch rocket mentioned by the officer at the beginning of this section. This rocket can be fired from artillery sites, from tactical fighters, or from helicopters.

The early 2.75 inch rocket, called the "Mighty Mouse," was intended for air-to-air missions. Air-to-surface versions for the Army were developed during 1963–1964. These versions have fragmentation warheads added to the rocket; some contain "flechettes" (slender projectiles capable of literally shredding flesh). Others contain "white phosphorus," an incendiary that ignites on contact with the air.

Some of the rockets are equipped with proximity fuses which cause above-the-ground explosions. These fuses are produced by Zenith Radio Corporation and Fairchild Camera and Instrument Corporation and KDI Precision Products. An even more sophisticated fuse sometimes used is the "jungle canopy penetration fuse" made by Avco.[9] It is com-

9. NARMIC, *Weapons for Counter-Insurgency*, American Friends Service Committee, Philadelphia, 1970, p. 50.

plete with sensitive antennas which register the top of the jungle and activate time-delay mechanisms. The rocket then explodes underneath the jungle foliage.

Anti-personnel mines are the land counterpart to the cluster and fragmentation bombs. Instead of assaulting the enemy from the air, they are planted and explode on the ground. Perhaps the most dramatic description of one is provided by Tompkins in *The Weapons of World War III:*

> [The Claymore mine] is a curved green plastic box about the size of a large book, filled with explosives and thousands of BB-sized steel balls. Mounted on metal legs and pointed with the convex side facing the enemy (helpfully stenciled: FRONT TOWARD ENEMY), the Claymore explodes forward—sending out a hail of steel and plastic fragments that literally mow down the grass in a path six feet wide and a hundred feet straight ahead.[10]

Claymore mines are made by Standard Kollsman Industries, Republic Corporation, and General Tire and Rubber Company.

Besides the Claymore mine, there is also the "gravel" mine, which is covered with canvas and contains lead azide.[11] This was developed by the

10. Tompkins, *The Weapons of World War III*, p. 116.
11. NARMIC, *Weapons for Counter-Insurgency*, p. 52.

Army under a program called Project Gravel, and these mines are used as part of an "electronic fence" set up to defend forts in South Vietnam.[12] Gravel mines have been manufactured by Trenton Textile, Lowenthal Manufacturing, Southeastern Distributing Company, DuPont, Hercules, Susquehanna Corporation, and Bemis Company.

A third widely used mine is known as the "Jumping Jack." This mine pops up into the air when it is activated and then sprays fragments over a wide area. The *Washington Post* recently reported that nine Australian soldiers were killed by their own Jumping Jack mines which had been stolen and set up by the Vietcong.[13] The character and effectiveness of anti-personnel mines can be altered in versions that are filled with white phosphorus.

Beside fragmentation bombs and land mines, there is one more category of anti-personnel weapon now being used in Vietnam. It includes flechette and Beehive projectiles. Eric Prokosch, an anthropology professor at the University of Wisconsin who did some of the early research on anti-personnel weapons and their manufacturers, describes them as follows:

> A flechette is like a small finishing nail, about an inch long, with four fins welded on the blunt end. A Beehive dart is similar but smaller. Several thousand flechettes or Beehive darts are

12. DMS in "Mines" section of the *Ordnance* volume.
13. "9 Australians Killed by Own Mines," *Washington Post*, March 2, 1970.

loaded in a canister. The canister is fired from a gun and it explodes in the air, projecting the darts nose first.[14]

A UPI correspondent in Vietnam has reported that these flechettes and Beehive darts have shredded Vietcong; and an AP correspondent quoted an officer who had seen them actually impale men to trees. The projectiles are usually fired from artillery sites. However, John S. Tompkins writes of a micro-jet being developed by a "California research firm" which contains a rocket and provides a self-propelled flechette projectile. Also in the development stage is a rifle called the Special Purpose Individual Weapon (SPIW) designed to fire flechette and Beehive projectiles.

14. Eric Prokosch, " 'Conventional' Killers," *The New Republic,* November 1, 1969, p. 18.

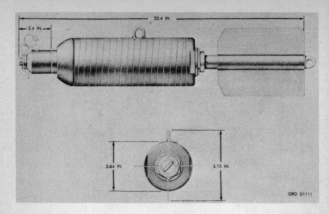

"An Early Twenty Pound Fragmentation Bomb, Similar to a Pineapple Bomb"

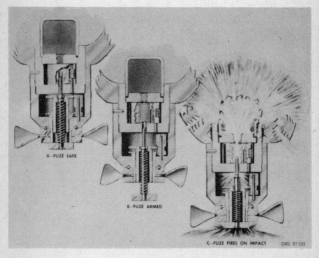

"Funtioning of a Bomb Round, Similar to a Pineapple Bomb"

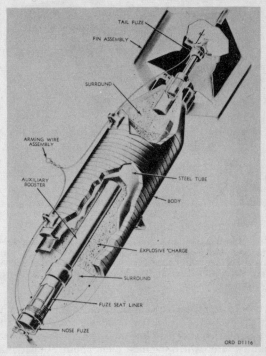

Labels on diagram: TAIL FUZE, FIN ASSEMBLY, SURROUND, ARMING WIRE ASSEMBLY, AUXILIARY BOOSTER, STEEL TUBE, BODY, EXPLOSIVE CHARGE, SURROUND, FUZE SEAT LINER, NOSE FUZE, ORD D1116

"260 Pound Fragmentation Bomb"
260 Pound Fragmentation Bombs Were Dropped
on the village of Deduc in November, 1965 killing 48 South Vietnamese civilians and wounding
55.

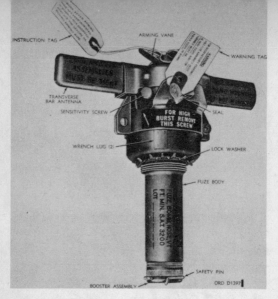

"Cross-Section of a Proximity Fuse"

Credit: Department of the Army, the Navy, and the Air Force: *Bombs and Bomb Components,* Department of the Army Technical Manual, TM 9-1325-200, Department of the Navy Publication, NAVWEPS OP 3530, Department of AF Technical Order, TO 11-1-26. April, 1966.

Guava bomblet, showing steel balls on outside casing. On the right is half of a guava bomblet, showing interior where explosive and fuse are put. The bomblets contain proximity fuses which explode them about 30 feet in the air, causing from 300 to 600 steel pellets to shower down, spraying the ground and effectively penetrating bunkers. Some types are fitted with delayed action fuses, however, and go off later when people have come out from their bunkers.

Credit: R. Neubert.

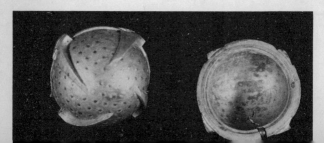

48.7-IN MAX

RA PD 257422

2.75 Inch High-Explosive Rocket

Credit: Department of the Army, *Rockets,* Department of the
Army Technical Manual, TM 9-1950. February, 1958.

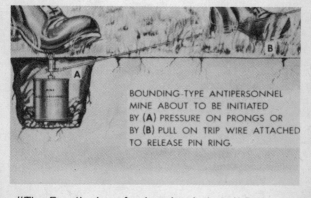

BOUNDING-TYPE ANTIPERSONNEL
MINE ABOUT TO BE INITIATED
BY (A) PRESSURE ON PRONGS OR
BY (B) PULL ON TRIP WIRE ATTACHED
TO RELEASE PIN RING.

"The Functioning of a Jumping Jack Anti-Personnel
Mine"

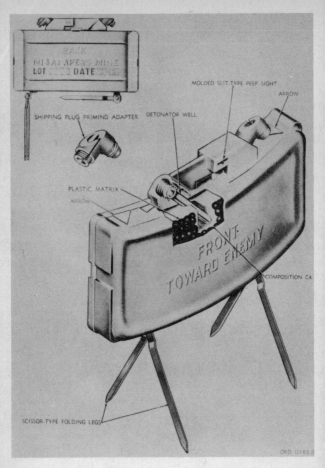

"A Claymore Anti-Personnel Mine, M18A1"

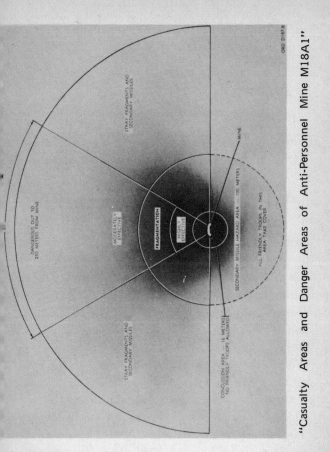

ORD D187-B

"Casualty Areas and Danger Areas of Anti-Personnel Mine M18A1"

2. The Nature of Anti-Personnel Weapons

As mentioned in the introduction to this study, anti-personnel weapons are only one group within a series of conventional munitions developed or adapted for limited wars and presently in full use in Vietnam. The series includes miniguns, defoliants, gases, napalm, the pattern bombing of Boeing B-52's and the M-16 rifle and several other less-known weapons. [For further details on these weapons, see the Appendix.]

Anti-personnel bombs, mines, and flechettes were selected for detailed study because their effect on "targets" is particularly brutal. No other conventional weapon group has the same high fragmentation capability, speed or power of impact. The International War Crimes Tribunal, organized in 1967 by Bertrand Russell, described the devastating wounds caused by anti-personnel fragments:

Their penetration power in the human body . . . is very great. The same individual may be struck by several fragments: each of them must be removed surgically. As the trajectory of these projectiles is long and irregular inside the body, the lesions caused by one fragment alone are numerous, varied, difficult to detect and require delicate operations. The failure of the surgeon to recognize one of the lesions can be fatal.[1]

White phosphorus added to the bombs and mines multiplies the damaging capacity. Frank Harvey has written:

White phosphorus bombs were another incendiary the VC feared greatly. This stuff is even more vicious than napalm. In the civilian hospital in Can Tho, I saw a man who had a piece of white phosphorus in his flesh. It was still burning.[2]

Surgeons have had to devise drastic new operative procedures for dealing with anti-personnel weapon injuries. Robert Crichton, in a review of *Air War: Vietnam*, recounts that:

A CBU victim, if hit in the stomach, is simply slit from the top of the stomach to the bottom and the contents of the stomach emptied out

1. Arlette El Kaim-Sartre, "A Summary of the Evidence and the Judgments: An Introduction," *On Genocide*, p. 21.
2. Harvey, *Air War: Vietnam*, pp. 56–57.

on a table and fingered through for "frags". . .
When the sorting is done the entrails are re-
placed and the stomach sewed back up like a
football. This "football scar" has become the
true badge of misery in South Vietnam.[3]

Not only do anti-personnel weapons produce heinous
injury to targets within their striking range, but a
large number of these targets are civilians. In the
three and one-half years preceding the March 1968
bombing halt, North Vietnam's civilian casualty toll
has been estimated at 200,000 per year. The Russell
War Crimes Tribunal documented the fact that U.S.
bombing targets in the North included dikes, hydraulic structures, hospitals, various medical, educa-
tional and religious institutions, and populous cities
and villages with industrial and agricultural plants.[4]

A *Life* writer, Lee Lockwood, gave an eye-witness
account of extensive destruction in North Vietnam
from anti-personnel weapon fire:

The most convincing evidence of CBUs I saw
was near Viet Tri northwest of Hanoi. Here,
factory walls were scarred with characteristic
symmetrical patterns of pockmarks. Later I
visited the Viet Tri hospital, which recently had
been moved from the city to a rural village

3. Robert Crichton, "Our Air War," *The New York Review
of Books,* Jan. 4, 1968, p. 3.
4. El Kaim-Sartre, "A Summary," pp. 16–19.

several miles away. On January 18, according to Dr. Le Hau Suu, even this village had been bombed with CBUs. Pellet marks scarred the doctor's desk, chair, cabinet, sterilizer and other instruments. Outside, the crumpled half-shell of a cannister lay across the narrow dike in a field stippled with cup-sized craters. The doctor rounded up several patients he said had been wounded by the pellets. One 18-year-old girl had taken a pellet through her left arm, one in her intestine, one through her finger and lower lip, and one which I could feel with my fingers embedded in the heel of her hand.[5]

In South Vietnam, the civilian war casualty toll has also been very high. Senator Edward Kennedy's Senate Subcommittee on Refugees estimated that there are about 150,000 to 200,000 civilians injured or killed each year in South Vietnam.

The indiscriminate nature of anti-personnel bombs, mines and projectiles is a partial reason for the high civilian toll. Because of the wide area coverage, it is not possible to distinguish between soldiers and the regular civilian population.

Bombing strikes in South Vietnam are directed by the Forward Air Controllers (known as FAC's). They cruise over the jungle and the countryside in small two-seater planes, Cessna 0-1 "Bird-Dog" or the more recent and improved Cessna 0-2, provid-

5. Lee Lockwood, "Recollections of Four Weeks with the Enemy," *Life*, April 7, 1967.

ing visual reconnaissance and directing the attacks of the high-speed tactical fighters.

The FAC's direct "pre-planned" attacks by marking targets with white-phosphorus, napalm, or smoke bombs. In addition, they call for spontaneous attacks as a result of their own reconnaissance. All strikes require the approval of the local Vietnamese provincial chief. Frank Harvey cites examples of FAC pilots who became disillusioned with their jobs because civilians were so often the victims of the attacks which they directed. He reported that one pilot

> had been relieved of duty because he had openly declared himself guilty of assisting in killing many civilians.[6]

Another pilot directed fire for a pre-planned attack into a rice paddy because there were civilians in the village scheduled for bombing. While there is no way to establish from public information the exact number of civilian casualties resulting from anti-personnel weapons, it is fairly certain that they account for a significant number of the civilian casualties in both North and South Vietnam.

Anti-personnel weapons have also been used mistakenly in many incidents. One such case was reported in the *New York Times* in November, 1965:

6. Harvey, *Air War: Vietnam,* p. 62.

. . . A Vietnamese officer transposed the first two numerals of a grid coordinate, or map-reading code, thus directing two United States fighter-bombers to the village of Deduc rather than to a Viet Cong guerilla concentration six miles farther west. . .

The planes . . . killed 48 South Vietnamese civilians and wounded 55 with 260-pound frag-mentation bombs and white-phosphorus fire bombs. . .

. . . Deduc, the bombed village, is near the South China Sea, a little more than 300 miles northeast of Saigon.[7]

A similar incident was quoted in a dispatch from Saigon on July 2, 1966:

Eight Vietnamese civilians—seven of them chil-dren—were killed and 52 persons wounded yes-terday when a U.S. plane accidentally bombed a village, an Air Force investigation shows.

The spokesman gave this account: "The acci-dent took place when three U.S. F100 Super-sabre jet fighter-bombers jettisoned unused ex-plosives while returning from a mission south of Saigon.

"Two of the planes jettisoned their canisters of anti-personnel bombs successfully over a de-serted section of the Dong Hoa River, about

one mile northeast of the village [near Bien
Hoa].

"But one canister from the third plane dropped
into the village market place and exploded in a
two-room private elementary school containing
a teacher and 50 pupils.

"One pilot later reported he had noticed that
one of the canisters he was jettisoning appar-
ently stuck for a second before it fell."[8]

One further factor raising the civilian toll has been
the indiscriminate usage of anti-personnel bombs in
the so-called "free fire" zones of the South. Free
fire zones (also named "free bomb zones" or "free
strike zones") are areas of heavy enemy concentration or areas which are heavily influenced by the
Vietcong. U.S. policy assumes that all persons in
these areas are the enemy and gives free rein to
pilots to shoot anything that moves. The intention is
simply to make the area unsafe for the Vietcong
and thereby deny them that land base. Unfortu-
nately, the Vietnamese peasants fail to view this
policy as simply as U.S. military commanders do.
The peasants find themselves left with just two
terrible choices. If they remain on their land, the
land they have lived on all their lives, they will be
considered the enemy, fired upon and more than

8. Quoted in *In The Name of America*, Clergy and Laymen
Concerned about the War, p. 224. The news service cited does
not permit attribution outside the pages of its client news-
papers.

likely killed. The alternative is to leave their land, become refugees, and eventually be relocated in one of the increasingly numerous refugee camps in South Vietnam.

The Armed Forces have developed and distributed numerous pamphlets and leaflets communicating this "free choice" to the peasants.

One example was described by Jonathan Schell, now an editor of *The New Yorker*, who spent the summer of 1967 with the U.S. Armed Forces in Vietnam and wrote a book titled *The Military Half:*

The text of the leaflet, like that of all such leaflets, is printed, of course, in Vietnamese. On one side there are two cartoon drawings. The first shows several soldiers of the Vietcong setting up a mortar position near a thatched-roofed house while another soldier leans out of a window firing an automatic weapon. A woman holding a child by the hand stands next to the house. Under the picture, a caption reads, "If the Vietcong do this . . . " The second picture shows an Air Force jet pulling out of its dive over the house. An explosion in front of the house has thrown the soldiers and the woman and her child to the ground, and the house is aflame. In the foreground a man lies on the earth, clutching his chest. Streams of blood flow from his eyes, nostrils, mouth and ears. The rest of the pamphlet is in black and white, but this blood is printed in red ink. The second caption, completing the unfinished sentence of the first, reads, " . . . your village will look like this." On the other side is a text reading:

Dear Citizens:

The U.S. Marines are fighting alongside the Government of Vietnam forces in Duc Pho in order to give the Vietnamese people a chance to live a free, happy life, without fear of hunger and suffering. But many Vietnamese have paid with their lives and their homes have been destroyed because they helped the Vietcong in an attempt to enslave the Vietnamese people. Many hamlets have been destroyed because these villages harbored the Vietcong.

The hamlets of Hai Mon, Hai Tan, Sa Binh, Tan Binh, and many others have been destroyed because of this. We will not hesitate to destroy every hamlet that helps the Vietcong, who are powerless to stop the combined might of the G.V.N. and its allies.

The U.S. Marines issue this warning: THE U.S. MARINES WILL NOT HESITATE TO DESTROY IMMEDIATELY ANY VILLAGE OR HAMLET HARBORING THE VIETCONG. WE WILL NOT HESITATE TO DESTROY, IMMEDIATELY, ANY VILLAGE OR HAMLET USED AS A VIETCONG

STRONGHOLD TO FIRE AT OUR TROOPS
OR AIRCRAFT.

The choice is yours. If you refuse to let the
Vietcong use your villages and hamlets as their
battlefield, your homes and your lives will be
saved.

Peaceful citizens, stay in your homes. Deny
your support to the V.C.s.[9]

(Other samples of these leaflets are contained else-
where in *The Military Half* and in another book by
Jonathan Schell, *The Village of Ben Suc.*)

The natural outcome of this policy is that the
peasants are subjected to military reprisals by the
Vietcong if they fail to cooperate. They are subjected
to U.S. bombings if they do cooperate with the
VCs, or they are subjected to U.S. bombings just
because they choose to remain in their homes.

Anti-personnel weapons are among the ordnance
items that are used in free fire zones; consequently,
it is reasonable to expect that they have been responsible for a sizeable percentage of the civilian
casualties that have occurred in these areas.

9. Jonathan Schell, *The Military Half*, p. 17–18.

3. An Analysis of Company Involvement in Anti-Personnel Weapons

Anti-personnel weapons contracting amounts to less than 1% annually of the total Department of Defense budget. Yet 105 U.S. companies have been involved in this contracting. There are several reasons why the company list is so long. First of all, there is a wide variety of anti-personnel weapons. Secondly, with the exception of Honeywell and General Tire and Rubber Company, no single firm makes an entire weapons system. Each company makes only a component. In the case of cluster bombs, for example, one company may make the "mother" bomb, another the bomblets, and another the fuses. Still another company may have a contract for "loading, packing and assembling" the whole system. As a result, many companies have become involved in this relatively small segment of defense contracting.

The Research and Development
of Anti-Personnel Weapons

Government encouragement and support for the development and production of anti-personnel weapons and other conventional arms has not been caused entirely by the U.S. position in Vietnam, as Cecil Brownlow, in *Aviation Week and Space Technology*, points out:

> Vietnam . . . is only one reason behind the growing emphasis on conventional tactical warfare. An equal spur is the belief in top Pentagon circles that limited rather than nuclear wars will pose the greatest threat to the U.S. over the next 10-15 years.[1]

The research and development work on weapons has been and is being done by various military and civilian engineers in Defense Department laboratories in conjunction with private industry. Some of the early research was conducted during the 1950's at the Ballistic Research Laboratories at the Aberdeen (Maryland) Proving Ground. One study done there was concerned with "Provisional Values of the Vulnerability of Personnel to Fragments" (1951). Another, the same year, was "A Method for Computing the Number of Casualties to be Inflicted by

1. "Limited War Problems Challenge Industry," *Aviation Week and Space Technology*, March 14, 1966, p. 26.

Fragments from an Airburst Shell or Bomb." A study entitled "The Probability of Incapacitation by a Steel Sphere or by Darts When Portions of the Body are Rendered Invulnerable" was done in 1956.[2]

Aberdeen, Maryland is also the location of the Army's Limited War Laboratory, which is responsible for developing new weapons for limited war. One of the projects there involves training pigeons and bedbugs as scouts for search and destroy missions in Vietnam.[3]

Another laboratory for developing and testing conventional weapon systems is the Air Proving Ground at Elgin Air Force Base in Florida. *Aviation Week and Space Technology* calls Elgin:

> . . . a vital market place where industry can learn of new limited war requirements from, and make known its capabilities to, those Air Force organizations with a strong voice in making limited-war-items decisions.[4]

Elgin is also the testing ground for cluster bomb dispensers. The December 11, 1967, issue of *Aviation Week and Space Technology* showed photographs and provided descriptions of such tests.[5]

2. Cited in Prokosch's " 'Conventional' Killers," p. 21.
3. William Beecher, "Way-Out Weapons," *New York Times Sunday Magazine,* March 24, 1968, p. 49ff.
4. "Limited War Weapons Tested at Elgin AFB," *Aviation Week and Space Technology,* Mid-December, 1966, p. 36ff.
5. "Bomb Dispensers Help USAF Match Ordnance Targets," *Aviation Week and Space Technology,* December 11, 1967, p. 79.

We now turn to a consideration of company involvement in the production of anti-personnel weapons.

Companies That Make an Entire Weapons System

In a large portion of defense contracting, one contractor is chosen for manufacturing a weapons system or military item. For example, in the contracting for airplanes, Lockheed is building the C-5A and General Dynamics built, or tried to build, the F-111's. In anti-personnel weapons contracting, there are two companies which make entire weapons systems. General Tire and Rubber Company has two divisions which make entire cluster bomb systems: Batesville Manufacturing Company makes CBU-30/A's and Aerojet-General makes CBU-38/A's. Honeywell manufactures several complete cluster bomb systems: the Rockeye II cluster bombs, CBU-34/A's, CBU-42/A's and CBU-55/B's.[6]

Honeywell also produces anti-personnel mines and dispensers. Honeywell informed its stockholders of this work in the following manner:

Conventional weapon programs promising steady growth potential in future years include the Navy's Rockeye munition-dispenser system

6. DMS in the *Ordnance* volume.

and several aerially-delivered mine-dispenser systems which went into volume production this year.[7]

Consumer-Oriented Companies

A large number of companies involved in contracting for anti-personnel weapons and their components are consumer-oriented. These are companies which the layman or the private investor would not expect to find producing military weapons. Among them are: Beech Aircraft, D. H. Baldwin, Brunswick Corp., Bulova Watch Co., Hamilton Watch Co., Household Finance, Reynolds Metals Co., Uniroyal, Whirlpool, Wurlitzer Corp. and Zenith Radio Corp. Military business, and specifically anti-personnel weapon production, really constitutes an "aside" for these companies, whose focus and major profit source are products they sell to consumers. Revenues derived from military production are, in most cases, not essential to the company's successful profit performance.

U.S. watch companies provide a particularly interesting example of a consumer-oriented industry deeply involved in defense contracting. Watch companies have been able to survive in this country only because of government protection from the competition of foreign (mainly Swiss) watch companies. Foreign watches are made by skilled work-

7. "Good Americans," *The Nation,* July 8, 1968.

ers who do not receive nearly as high a wage as comparably skilled American workers. As a result, foreign watches are considerably cheaper to produce and sell than domestic watches of the same quality. But the U.S. government protects the watch industry with one of the highest tariffs placed on any U.S. import—a tariff approximating 40% ad valorem.

The question immediately arises: why does the government offer such heavy subsidization to the watch industry (or, as they like to refer to themselves, the horological industry)? One important rationale was summarized in a report by the Preparedness Subcommittee of the Armed Services Committee:

> The highly skilled workers in the American watch and clock industry, who require long years of training and experience, and their unique ability to develop and produce within the shortest time possible, precision instruments to minute tolerances, are essential to the national defense. Therefore, it is in the interest of national defense to keep this essential industry alive and vital.[8]

This rationale has, at least in some cases, been accepted by the industry itself. In a 1955 testimony before Congress, Mr. Arde Bulova, then Chairman

8. *Jewel Substitutes in Watch Movements*, Hearings Before the Committee on Ways and Means, House of Representatives, July 27–28, 1955, p. 55.

of the Board of Bulova Watch Company, included
it in his argument for increased tariffs on jewelled
movements imported into the United States. He said:

> If there is ever another mobilization or an-
> other war, I warn you that Switzerland in all
> likelihood would be engulfed by the forces of
> communism; in any event, it would not be able
> to maintain its neutrality to the extent of using
> the Swiss watch industry to supply the high-
> precision needs of the industry in the United
> States of America.[9]

The skilled workers in watch companies are, to a
great extent, protected by the government so that
they will be available to produce components for
military weapons when needed. These workers produce jewelled movements for avionics systems and
for the space program. They also make fuses for
ordnance systems. Bulova Watch Company and
Hamilton Watch Company, for example, manufacture components (fuses) for anti-personnel weapons.
Every major American watch manufacturer, with the
exception of Elgin,[10] does some kind of military
work.

Unimpeded foreign competition would ordinarily
drive down the price of watches made in this country. It would also probably force some domestic

9. Ibid. p. 56.
10. Elgin dropped all military business in 1965 (Moody's
Industrial Manual).

watch companies out of business. Or it would force them to accelerate the already extant practice of establishing plants in foreign countries, such as Switzerland and Jamaica, where they could take advantage of cheaper labor. Because of this "defense-inspired" government subsidy which hinders foreign competition, American consumers pay greatly inflated prices for their watches.*

In the past few years, the watch industry has been losing its exclusive position in contracting with the Department of Defense for horological-type products. Other companies, including Fairchild Camera and Instrument Company, Avco Corp. and Zenith Radio Corp. have moved into the area of producing sophisticated fuse mechanisms for antipersonnel weapons. As a result, President Johnson rescinded in 1967 an additional tariff rate which had been instituted in 1954 to raise the watch tariff even higher than the 40% now in effect. The decision to rescind the rate was based on a study done by the Office of Emergency Preparedness at the request of the President. Farris Bryant, Director of the OEP, submitted the study to the President in November, 1966. His conclusion stated:

* NOTE: This is only one industrial example out of many of government subsidies through tariff protection for purposes of national security. Oil companies are another: they are "protected" from foreign competition by tariffs on oil imports and by the oil import quota program which places an absolute limit on the amount of oil that can be imported into the U.S. every year. The rationale is that we must protect our domestic producers of oil so that in case of a national emergency we will be assured of adequate supplies of oil.

. . . that watches, watch movements and watch
parts are not being imported into the United
States in such quantities or under such circum-
stances as to threaten or impair the national
security. I have also concluded, based on
studies and judgements of the interested defense agencies, that the domestic watch manufacturers will be likely to continue production
of defense materials for the foreseeable future,
that the non-horological industry now has and
will continue to have a role in the production
of essential military timing devices, and that
horological-type defense items will continue to
be available from one source or another without regard to the level of imports of watches,
movements and parts.[11]

The Council on Economic Priorities has attempted
to get the watch companies' view of their own involvement in anti-personnel weapons production. A
questionnaire was sent to watch companies and to
other companies that have anti-personnel weapon
contracts for fuses. In addition, a questionnaire was
sent to several watch companies that do not have
anti-personnel contracts with the Pentagon. To date,
no replies have been received. The questionnaires
were sent out in the early part of March, 1970.

11. "Memorandum to the President" in *Foreign Trade and
Tariff Proposals,* Hearings Before the House Ways and Means
Committee, June–July, 1968, p. 3739.

Companies That Are
Major Military Contractors

A sizeable number of the companies that produce anti-personnel weapons are also large defense contractors. The following have been among the top 100 defense contractors during the past two fiscal years:

Aluminum Co. of America
American Manufacturing Co. of Texas
A-T-O (formerly "Automatic" Sprinkler Corp. of
　America)
Avco
Cessna Aircraft
Chamberlain Manufacturing Co.
City Investing
Day and Zimmerman
du Pont
FMC
General Motors
General Tire and Rubber Co.
Hercules
Honeywell
Martin Marietta (Harvey Aluminum, a recently-
　acquired subsidiary, was also listed among the
　top 100 defense contractors while it was an in-
　dependent company.)
Mason and Hanger
Motorola
Norris Industries

Northrop
Sperry Rand
Standard Oil Co. (New Jersey)
Susquehanna
Talley Industries (see note, page 105, on the in-
    depth company profile of General Time Corp.)
Thiokol Chemical Corp.
Uniroyal
Westinghouse
Whittaker[12]

Broader Issues

In looking at the U.S. corporations that produce
anti-personnel weapons, some broader issues related
to the whole area of defense contracting arise. They
deserve to be mentioned and considered.

Use of Government-Owned
Property and Equipment

First, a sizeable amount of defense work is done on
government-owned machinery, which is leased to
private contractors. Senator William Proxmire, who
has done substantial research on this subject,
charged in January, 1968, that some 23 companies
were making improper use of Defense Dept. prop-

12. Dept. of Defense, "100 Companies and Their Subsidiary Corporations Listed According to Net Value of Military
Prime Contract Awards," Fiscal years (FY) 1968 and 1969.

erty. He cited evidence from a GAO investigation to substantiate his charge that the Defense Dept. had been lax in enforcing regulations concerning the property and that the companies had been using the property for commercial uses without paying adequate rentals. Among the companies cited by Proxmire were four manufacturers of anti-personnel weapons: Aerojet-General (a division of General Tire and Rubber Co.), Beech Aircraft Corporation, Sperry Gyroscope Company (a division of Sperry Rand) and FMC Corporation. Assistant Secretary of Defense Thomas Morris stated that Proxmire's charges were out of proportion. He said that in 5 of the 23 cases, the Pentagon found that the contractors owed small additional rentals, $60,000 in all. Nevertheless, he acknowledged that some of the Government Accounting Office complaints were valid, and announced plans to tighten restrictions regarding use of government property.

Contract Irregularities

In recent years, the methods involved in military contracting have come under question. The Joint Economic Committee, in its investigations of military contracting, found that there have been numerous instances of excess profits being made by defense contractors and that there have been some irregularities in contract procedures. An example of this sort of problem is provided, with respect to anti-personnel weapons contracting, by Alsco, Inc. (recently acquired by Harvard Industries of Farmingdale, New Jersey).

Alsco made launchers for 2.75 inch rockets for the Navy. In March of 1968, the Justice Department began an investigation of Alsco for

> . . . suspected irregularities, arising out of ar-
> rangements among certain officials of the com-
> pany and a subcontractor, of a significant na-
> ture involving items of expenses under govern-
> ment contracts negotiated over a period of 3
> years.[13]

Alsco was immediately placed on a suspended bid-
der's list pending the result of the investigation. In August, Alsco and the subcontractor, Chromcraft Corporation, which was merged into Alsco in June of 1966, and four persons were indicted by a Federal Grand Jury for conspiracy to defraud the gov-
ernment of $4 million. The defendants were charged with setting up two dummy corporations which mas-
queraded as subcontractors. The dummy firms trans-
mitted false invoices to Chromcraft and Alsco which, in turn, submitted them to the Navy and received payment. The money was then transferred back to the dummy corporations and then maneuvered into Swiss bank accounts. Two weeks before the indictment, the Navy had awarded Alsco a $13.9 million

13. "President Quits, US Probe," *Wall Street Journal*, April 8, 1968, p. 11.

contract for launchers despite the fact that Alsco was on the suspended bidder's list.[14]

The Navy maintained that it was necessary to give the contract to Alsco because of war needs and because Alsco was the sole supplier of the needed launchers. Later, in 1969, the Army developed a new launcher, the XM200, to replace the Alsco launcher. This launcher is now being manufactured by the A. C. Electronics Division of General Motors, and Brunswick Corp.

On February 10, 1970, a federal judge in Washington sentenced the four individuals who had been indicted by the grand jury in August for conspiracy to defraud the government. All four had pleaded guilty. The four were: Andrew L. Stone, past president and chief stockholder of Alsco; Evelyn R. Price, Stone's executive secretary; Francis N. Rosenbaum, a Washington lawyer and a former director of Alsco; and Robert B. Bregman, president of Bregman Electronics of New York. Bregman's firm was one of the dummy firms referred to in the indictment. Stone and Rosenbaum received sentences of ten years; and Miss Price and Bregman received five-year sentences. Additionally, Alsco pleaded guilty to the charge and was fined $5,000. The Justice Department has also filed a civil damage suit against Alsco in the Federal District Court in St. Louis for giving the government inflated cost data. Finally, the company, Stone and Miss Price have all pleaded guilty

14. "US Charges Fraud," *New York Times,* August 8, 1968, p. 2.

to conspiring to export launchers to a Belgian company without the required export license or State Department approval. Alsco was fined $25,000 for this offense and Stone and Miss Price were sentenced on April 3 in St. Louis. Stone received a five-year jail sentence, not to begin until he has completed his ten-year term for fraud, and a $10,000 fine. Miss Price received a five-year sentence.

Also, on February 13, 1970, Harvard Industries announced that it had filed suit against former Alsco officials, including Stone, for misstatements and for concealment of facts concerning Alsco's financial condition. It also alleged that it faces numerous suits [which could ultimately cost the company "many millions of dollars"] because of Alsco's actions prior to the merger of the two companies.

4. The Technical Designations of Anti-Personnel Weapons

In order to identify the anti-personnel weapons that the different companies manufacture, it is necessary to describe the technical designations given to them by the Department of Defense. These technical designations are used by DMS in its reports on defense contracting for ordnance items. It will also be helpful to be aware of the various components contained in the different anti-personnel weapons. The following section lists all of the manufacturers of anti-personnel weapons. This section is intended to aid the reader in interpreting the contract information in that section.

First, the cluster bomb units are all designated CBUs. Every CBU consists of several parts: the "Suspended Underwing Unit," or SUU, refers to the bomb dispenser (the "mother" bomb) and BLUs are the bomblets themselves (DMS does not specify what

BLU stands for—perhaps "Bomblet Unit"). A dispenser plus a certain type of bomblet makes a CBU. For example, the CBU-46 consists of a SUU-7C/A bomb dispenser (made by Cessna, Beech, Automatic Sprinkler, and Brunswick) and BLU-66/B bomblets (made by General Tire and Rubber Company).

There is some amount of difficulty in translating these technical designations into the more graphic terminology that has been employed to report the usage of these weapons in the war in Vietnam. The terms "guava" and "pineapple" were coined by the Vietnamese to describe the weapons that were being used against them—after all, they were not aware of the numbers assigned to these bombs by the Pentagon. However, a few technical designations have been identified.[1] The CBU-24/B is a "guava" bomb. It consists of SUU-30 dispensers and BLU-26/B or BLU-36/B bomblets. SUU-30 dispensers are made by General Tire and Rubber Company, City Investing Corporation, Tyler Corporation and Temco. The "guava" bomblets are made by the following companies: Adventure Line Manufacturing Company, Ajax Hardware Manufacturing Company, Gibbs Die Casting Aluminum Corporation, Honeywell, National Lead Company, Superior Steel Ball Company, and Victor Comptometer Corporation.

Some additional designations which can be identified are the following: the SUU-30 dispensers are in

---

1. Prokosch, " 'Conventional' Killers" and Crichton, "Our Air War."

the "Sadeye" series of cluster bombs and SUU-38/A and SUU-45/A are Tactical Fighter Dispenser Munitions. The TFDM's are manufactured by Honeywell. There are, consequently, several SUU, BLU, and CBU designations which remain unidentified in terms of popular terminology. However, all of these designations do refer to anti-personnel fragmentation weapons.

The Beehive and flechette projectiles are designated as 90mm or 105mm projectiles. They are made by Kissell Company, Norris Industries, Northrop Corporation, Skagit Corporation, and Whirlpool. AAI, Honeywell, Northrop and Whirlpool have had contracts dealing with the development of the Special Purpose Individual Weapon (SPIW) for firing these projectiles.

The contracting for 2.75 inch rockets involves several companies. There are three varieties of launchers for the rockets, each with its own technical designation—M158 launchers made by the Rois Manufacturing Company and by the A. C. Electronics Division of General Motors, M157 launchers made by Alsco, Inc., and the XM200 launchers made by A. C. Electronics; Norris Industries and Alcoa make tubes for launching the rockets. Whittaker Corporation makes igniters for the rockets. Ametek makes stabilizer rods.

D. H. Baldwin has received contracts for merely loading, packing, and assembling 2.75 inch rocket motors. Applied Devices Corporation, HITCO, Hoffman Electronics Corporation, and Alco Standard have all contracted for fin and nozzle assemblies.

There are also several types of fuses used in 2.75 inch rockets: M423 impact fuses made by Bulova Watch Company, General Time, and Avco Corporation; M429 electronic proximity fuses made by KDI Precision Products, Fairchild Camera and Instrument Corporation, and Zenith Radio Corporation; M427 impact fuses made by KDI Precision Products and General Time; and the "jungle canopy penetration fuse" made by Avco.

Finally, there are various types of warheads for these rockets: M151 warheads weigh 10 pounds and are made by Hayes-Albion, City Investing Corporation, Medico Industries, General Tire and Rubber Company, and Airport Manufacturing Corporation; M229 warheads weigh 17 pounds and are made by Medico Industries and Lehigh, Inc.; and WDU-4A/A flechette warheads are made by Northrop Corporation.

Among the numerous technical designations for anti-personnel weapons, the M18 and M18A1 Claymore mines are made by Standard Kollsman Industries, Republic Corporation, and General Tire and Rubber Company. The gravel mines, XM22, XM27 and XM45E1, are made by Trenton Textile, Lowenthal Manufacturing, Southeastern Distributing Company, duPont, Hercules, Susquehanna Corporation, and Bemis Company. A linear electrical anti-personnel mine, the XM37, was developed at the Picatinny Arsenal—there is no information to date on contractors. Anti-personnel mines, XM41 and XM41E1, are made by FMC, Trenton Textile, Hercules, Susquehanna, and Southeastern Distributing. XM54 mines are filled with white phosphorus and have a Jumping Jack action; they are manufactured by Honeywell, Standard Kollsman Industries, VIZ Manufacturing, and Rocket Research Corporation. XM57 mines are electronic and are made by Standard Kollsman and VIZ Manufacturing. The *Washington Post* article on the Jumping Jack mine said that its technical designation was M16; however, no contract information has been obtained on M16 anti-personnel mines.

The Manufacturers of
Anti-Personnel Weapons

CORPORATIONS	VALUE OF CONTRACTS
AAI Corp.	n.f.a.
ABG Instrument and Engineering Corp.	251,220
ACF Industries, Inc.	4,100,000
A-T-O, Inc. (formerly "Automatic" Sprinkler Corp.) *	2,700,000
Adventure Line Manufacturing Co.	3,300,000
Aeronca, Inc.	2,800,000
Airport Machining Corp.	9,400,000
Ajax Hardware Manufacturing Co.	135,000
Aladdin Heating Co.	197,600

* Companies that have been selected for detailed analysis in the following section of this study.

n.f.a.: No figures available.

Contract figures in excess of $1 million were rounded to the nearest $100,000. Exact dollar values were given for those less than $1 million.

Listings are by parent companies. Contract-holding subsidiaries are given in parentheses.

CORPORATIONS	VALUE OF CONTRACTS
Alco Standard Corp. (Jackson Products)*	10,600,000
Aluminum Co. of America*	11,400,000
American Manufacturing Co. of Texas	1,000,000
American Standard, Inc. (Melpar, Inc.)	n.f.a.
Ametek, Inc.	2,600,000
Applied Devices (Muncie Gear Works)*	16,000,000
Armco Steel (HITCO & F.T.S.)*	17,400,000
Avco Corp.*	3,300,000
Bache Tool and Die Co. (Concept Industries)	477,511
D. H. Baldwin (Baldwin Electronics)*	4,800,000
Beech Aircraft*	5,600,000
Bemis Co. (Perry Industries)	233,987
Birma Products	159,807
Breed Corp.	750,000
Brunswick Corp.*	3,200,000
Bulova Watch Co., Inc.*	5,100,000
C & S Ball Bearing Machinery and Equipment Corp.	445,640
CCI Corp. (Marquardt Corp.)*	7,900,000
Cessna Aircraft*	12,600,000
Chamberlain Manufacturing Co.	3,600,000
City Investing Co. (American Electric and Hayes-International)*	8,900,000
Cornell Aeronautical Labs.	39,823
Day and Zimmerman	99,200,000
Diodes, Inc. (Microcom, Inc.)	92,818

CORPORATIONS	VALUE OF CONTRACTS
Douglas and Lomason Co.	2,300,000
E. I. duPont de Nemours, Inc.*	1,200,000
Fairchild Camera and Instrument Corp.*	3,100,000
Filters, Inc.	163,395
F. M. C. Corp.*	2,400,000
Franklin Institute	75,708
General Motors (AC Electronics)*	2,100,000
General Time Corp.*	13,900,000
General Tire and Rubber Co. (also Aerojet General and Batesville Mfg. Co.)*	64,400,000
Gentzler Tool and Die Corp.	221,099
Gibbs Die Casting Aluminum Corp.	1,500,000
Hamilton Watch, Inc.	2,300,000
Hammond Corp.*	3,800,000
Harvard Ind. (Alsco)*	3,300,000
Hayes-Albion*	8,500,000
Hercules, Inc.*	9,700,000
Hoffman Electronics Corp.*	9,100,000
Honeywell, Inc.*	268,900,000
Hoover Ball and Bearing Co.	1,300,000
Household Finance Co. (King-Seeley Thermos Co.)*	147,362
KDI Corp. (KDI Precision Products)*	10,900,000
Kelsey-Hayes Co.	1,000,000
Kilian Steel Ball Corp.	765,102
Kissell Co. (Kisco Corp.)*	13,400,000
Koehler and Sons	2,500,000

CORPORATIONS	VALUE OF CONTRACTS
Lansdowne Steel and Iron Co.	8,200,000
Lasko Metal Products	6,200,000
Lehigh, Inc.	3,200,000
Lowenthal Manufacturing Co.	383,332
Martin Marietta Corp.*	3,300,000
Silas Mason, Inc. (Mason and Hanger)	13,700,000
Medico Industries	7,100,000
Miller Research	288,308
Motorola, Inc.*	242,880
Nash-Hammond, Inc.	1,200,000
National Lead Co.*	9,100,000
National Union Electric Co.*	3,300,000
New Process Fibre Co.	n.f.a.
Norris Industries, Inc.*	15,900,000
Northrop Corp.*	11,700,000
Republic Corp.	1,600,000
Reynolds Metals Co.*	1,050,000
M. C. Ricciardi	1,400,000
Riker-Maxson Corp. (Maxson Electronics)	216,433
Rocket Research Co. (Explosives Corp. of America)	172,483
Rois Manufacturing Co.	178,360
Rubbermaid, Inc. (Fusion Rubbermaid)	1,400,000
Scovill Manufacturing Co.*	8,100,000
Skagit Corp.	265,825
Southeastern Distributing Co.	653,529

CORPORATIONS	VALUE OF CONTRACTS
Sperry Rand Corp.*	99,100,000
Standard Kollsman Industries (Kollsman Instruments)*	5,100,000
Stanford Research Institute	87,950
Standard Oil Co. (New Jersey) (Esso Research and Engineering)	n.f.a.
Sterling Commercial Steel Ball Corp.	1,500,000
Superior Steel Ball Co.	8,100,000
Susquehanna Corp. (Atlantic Research)*	10,100,000
Teledyne Corp. (Brown Engineering)	187,440
Temco, Inc. (Cullman Metalcraft)	6,300,000
Thiokol Chemical Corp.	727,469
Trenton Textile Engineering and Manufacturing Co.	288,708
Tyler Corp. (formerly Saturn Industries)*	17,700,000
Uniroyal, Inc.*	24,200,000
United Aerotest Labs, Inc.	n.f.a.
VIZ Manufacturing Co.	701,760
Victor Comptometer Corp.*	3,700,000
Waterbury Steel Ball Co.	73,800
Westinghouse Electric Co.	50,000
Whirlpool Corp.*	5,100,000
Whittaker Comp.*	24,400,000
Wurlitzer Corp.*	546,566
Zenith Radio Corp.*	7,900,000

6. Company Profiles

The following 105 companies have received contracts from the Defense Department for research and development, manufacture, or assembly and packing of anti-personnel weapons systems or components. We have given basic information about all of these companies: the location of the main offices and the major products manufactured by each firm. Information about the contracts includes when they were given, the value of each contract, and the component which each contract requests.

Forty-seven of these companies have been selected for detailed description. All of them are publicly owned; and in addition, each of these companies holds anti-personnel contracts valued in excess of $5 million, produces an entire anti-personnel weapons system, or is generally considered a consumer-oriented company. Several companies meet one or more of these criteria, but were not included in this section of the survey because they are privately held. These companies are: Day & Zimmerman, Lansdowne Steel & Iron Co., Lasko Metal Products, Silas Mason & Co., Medico

Industries, Superior Steel Ball Corp., Temco Inc., & Airport Machining Co.

For purposes of comparison, we have included financial data for all of these companies (sales and earnings statistics). Many of these companies are consumer-oriented and transact a relatively small amount of business with the Department of Defense. Brand names of consumer products of these corporations have been included for reference.

Price-earnings ratios were included so that prospective investors might have some means of comparing these companies with others in the same industry.

Addresses of corporate offices, research centers and manufacturing facilities have been included so that people may know whether anti-personnel weapons are being produced in their area. In many cases, these companies own domestic subsidiaries, some of which produce consumer goods or have anti-personnel contracts of their own. We have regarded these subsidiaries as part of their respective parent companies, have included the brand name goods they produce, and have listed their plant sites. However, the major focus of our study remains on the parent companies and overall policy makers.

We have also included the names of the corporate decision-makers: the directors and presidents, and have also listed the corporate affiliations of these men.

In addition, we have tried to convey some sense of each company's operation through relevant information such as quotes from executives or from their annual reports and analyses from business journals.

The information about the companies and executives was obtained from standard references: Moody's *Industrial Manual*, Standard and Poor's Surveys, Poor's *Guide to Corporations*, *Who's Who in America* and annual reports. The contract data were obtained from *DMS Market Intelligence Report*, a McGraw-Hill publication; a paper entitled *The Vietnam Profiteers*, compiled by Eric Prokosch, a professor of Anthropology at the University of Wisconsin; and *Defense Industry Bulletin*, a publication of the Defense Supply Agency. These are the best available public sources; to the best of our knowledge, they are accurate.

A-T-O, Inc.
(formerly "Automatic" Sprinkler Corp.)
1000 E. Edgarton
Cleveland, Ohio
(216) 526–9900

MAJOR PRODUCTS:

Sprinkler systems, hydraulic equipment, heavy industrial equipment, navigational equipment, air pollution detection systems, athletic equipment, military weapons and components

CONSUMER BRANDS:

Rawlings sports equipment, *Mascot* home and auto fire extinguishers, *Compact* vacuum cleaners, *Vanguard* fire alarms, *Sherwood* tent trailers, *Colonel Logan* ornamental iron products, *American La France* fire extinguishers

FINANCIAL DATA:

$ Millions	1969	1968	1967
Net Sales	378.9	325.2	242.3
Net Income	8.6	2.1	9.2
P/E Ratio		200+	51–18
Yr End Mkt Value	82.8		

ANTI-PERSONNEL CONTRACTS:

10/68—$2.0 million for SUU 7C/A dispensers
1/69—$744,374 for SUU–7C/A dispensers with containers

(A-T-O, Inc., continued)
OFFICERS AND DIRECTORS:

Chairman: Harry Figgie, Rocky River, Ohio
  (Director: Clark-Reliance Corp.)
President: James H. Goss, Rye, New York

OUTSIDE DIRECTORS:

Clifford V. Brockaw III: General partner, Eastman
  Dillon, Union Securities and Co.
Daniel T. Carroll: Vice-President, Booz, Allen and
  Hamilton
D. S. Coenen: President, Coenen and Co.
F. S. Cornell: Retired President, Dow-Smith Corp.
E. M. deWindt: Chairman, Eaton, Yale and Towne
George R. Herzog: Retired Chairman, Union Com-
  merce Bank of Cleveland
John Koster: Retired Senior Vice-President, Inter-
  state Engineering Co.
Russell McFall: Chairman and President, Western
  Union
Hans Rinderknecht: Chairman, Cosmos Bank, Zurich
H. Sibley, Jr.: President, Harper Sibley, Jr., Inc., Sib-
  ley Realty Corp., Sibley Brokerage Corp., Dietrich-
  Sibley Agency, Inc.

ANNUAL MEETING:

The annual meeting is usually held during June in
Cleveland, Ohio.

PLANTS:

Anti-personnel weapons are produced at the Dallas,

(A-T-O, Inc., continued)
Texas plant. Other plants are in Alabama, California, Georgia, Illinois, Indiana, Kentucky, Louisiana, Massachusetts, New Jersey, New York, Ohio, Rhode Island, Texas, Virginia, West Virginia and Wisconsin.

CORPORATE PHILOSOPHY:

Value Line magazine reports that A-T-O is one of the few conglomerates that has not slowed its search for likely prospects for consolidation into one of their six divisions: fire protection systems, fluid controls and hydraulic equipment, heavy equipment, electrical instruments, consumer and recreation goods or defense products.

ALCO STANDARD CORP.
Valley Forge, Pennsylvania 19481
(215) 666–0760

MAJOR PRODUCTS:

Electrical equipment, latex and rubber compounds, fertilizer, fungicides, insecticides, paper products, commercial stoves

CONSUMER BRANDS:

Minerva wax paper, *Copco, Monarch, Binghamton, Universal* papers, *Custom Coaches, Land Cruisers* campers, *Clauss* cutlery, *Walker* china, *Cleveland* kitchen equipment, *Broaster* commercial kitchen equipment

FINANCIAL DATA:

	$ Millions	9/30/69*	1968	1967
Net Sales		304.8	216.9	118.5
Net Income		10.0	7.5	4.9
P/E Ratio		26–14	35–15	25–7
Yr End Mkt Value		106.8		

ANTI-PERSONNEL CONTRACTS:

[Jackson Products, a subsidiary of Alco Standard, holds the contracts]
6 to 12/68—$7.2 million for fin and nozzle assemblies for 2.75 inch rockets.

* Alco Standard's annual accounting period ends on September 30 of each calendar year.

(Alco Standard Corp., continued)
10/69—$3.4 million for fin and nozzle assemblies for
  2.75 inch rockets

OFFICERS AND DIRECTORS:

Chairman/President: Tinkam Veale, II, Gates Mills,
  Ohio

OUTSIDE DIRECTORS:

Paul R. Frohring: Former President, General Bio-
  chemicals, Inc.
John F. Headly: President, Grant Building, Inc.
Dr. J. D. Leitch
Robert M. Barr
R. H. Potts: Executive Vice-President, Philadelphia
  National Bank
H. V. Schweitzer: Consultant, Ft. Lauderdale, Fla.
Edward H. DaCosta: President, Synthane-Taylor
  Corp.
Edward A. Kilroy, Jr.: President, Kilroy Structural
  Steel Co.

ANNUAL MEETING:

The annual meeting is held during January at the
corporate offices in Valley Forge.

PLANTS:

Jackson Products maintains a plant in Tampa, Florida.
Subsidiaries (operated as divisions) are: Miller
Chemical and Fertilizer Co.; Modern Equipment Co.;
Gas Machinery Co.; Pyronics, Inc.; Savory Equip-

(Alco Standard Corp., continued)

ment Co.; Rice-Chadwick Rubber Co.; Sperry Rubber and Plastics Co.; Standard Molding Corp.; RMF, Inc.; Garrett-Buchanan Co.; Synthane-Taylor Corp.; Kilroy Structural Steel Co.

Other subsidiaries are: Custom Coach Corp.; Land Cruiser Corp.; Cleveland Range Co.; Minerva Wax Paper Co.; Walker China Co.; Clauss Cutlery Co.; Copco Papers, Inc.; Monarch Paper Co.; Universal Paper Co.; LaSalle Messinger Paper Co.; Baldwin Paper Co.; Central Paper Co.; Ipsen Industrial & Highway Products; Broaster Co.; Davey Compressors Co.; Paper Corp. of US; Wheelock Lovejoy Co.; Triumph Electro Corp.; Milwaukee Machine Products. Alco owns or operates plants in: Tampa and Plant City, Fla.; Philadelphia, Hanover, Ephrata, Valley Forge, Oaks, Allentown, Reading, Lancaster and Pittsburgh, Pa.; Chattanooga, Tenn.; Frederick, White-Ford, Salisbury and Snow Hill, Md.; Charlestown, W. Va.; Rockford, Pecatonia, Rockton, Cherry Valley, Bellwood and Chicago, Ill.; Newark, N.J.; Dayton, Killbuck, Kent, Bellecenter, Cleveland, Columbus, Fremont, Minerva and Bedford, Ohio; Winchester, Va.; LaVerne, Cal.; Houston, Dallas, Ft. Worth, San Antonio and Austin, Texas; New York City and Binghamton, N.Y.; Appleton, Milwaukee and Mequon, Wisc.; Boston, Mass.

CORPORATE PHILOSOPHY:

Alco Standard actively pursues small, privately owned

(Alco Standard Corp., continued)

businesses. Chairman Tinkam Veale, II explained his philosophy in the June 8, 1969 edition of the *New York Times:* ". . . All too often owner-managers of small companies hit a plateau when sales reach the $5 million mark . . . The company's head finds himself devoting too much time to legal, accounting, administrative and financial problems that he simply is not equipped to handle." To solve this problem, Veale is operating a program whereby a company may join Alco as a "Partner in Profit" with such functions centralized in the main office. Thus far, over 40 companies have joined Alco's growing family and Veale continues to search for others which fit his company's goals.

ALUMINUM CO. OF AMERICA (ALCOA)
1501 Alcoa Building
Pittsburgh, Pennsylvania
(412) 553-4545

MAJOR PRODUCTS:

Number one U.S. producer of aluminum; bauxite mining; fabrication of aluminum products; housing development

CONSUMER BRANDS AND SERVICES:

Alcoa Wrap, *Wear-Ever* utensils, *Cutco* cutlery and buffet service

FINANCIAL DATA:

$ Millions	1969	1968	1967
Net Sales	1,545.2	1,352.8	1,360.8
Net Income	122.4	104.7	108.4
P/E Ratio	15–12	17–13	19–14
Yr End Mkt Value	1,526.7		

ANTI-PERSONNEL CONTRACTS:

$5.8 million for 2.75 inch rocket tubes

11/69—contract modification on above contract for $5.6 million

OFFICERS AND DIRECTORS:

Chairman: Frederick J. Close, Pittsburgh, Pennsylvania

(Aluminum Co. of America, continued)

President: John D. Harper, Pittsburgh, Pennsylvania (Director: Mellon National Bank and Trust Co., Metropolitan Life Insurance Co.)

OUTSIDE DIRECTORS:

John Mayer: Chairman, Mellon National Bank and Trust Co.; Vice-President, General Motors

Richard Mellon: President, T. Mellon & Sons

George Wyckoff: Vice-President, T. Mellon & Sons

Frank Magee: Retired Chairman, Aluminum Co. of America

I. W. Wilson: Former Chairman, Aluminum Co. of America

Paul L. Miller: President, First Boston Corp.

E. D. Brockett: Chairman, Gulf Oil Corp.

ANNUAL MEETING:

Annual meeting is held in April in Pittsburgh, Pennsylvania.

PLANTS AND FACILITIES:

Plants are located in Alcoa, Tenn.; Badin, N.C.; Benton, Ark.; Chicago, Ill.; Chillicothe, Ohio; Cleveland, Ohio; Corona, Cal.; Cressona, Pa.; Davenport, Iowa; Evansville, Ind.; Fort Wayne, Ind.; Franklin, N.C.; Lafayette, Ind.; Lancaster, Pa.; Laurinburg, N.C.; Lebanon, Pa.; Los Angeles, Cal.; Marshall, Texas; Massena, N.Y.; Mobile, Ala.; New Kensington, Pa.; New York, N.Y.; Point Comfort, Texas; Richmond,

(Aluminum Co. of America, continued)
Ind.; Rockdale, Texas; Tifton, Ga.; Vancouver, Wash.;
Wenatchee, Wash.

Research and Development facilities are located in
Chicago, Ill.; Cleveland, Ohio; East St. Louis, Ill.;
Fort Wayne, Ind.; Marshall, Texas; Massena, N.Y.;
Merwin, Pa.; New Kensington, Pa.; Richmond, Ind.

Real Estate Operations are Allegheny Center, Pittsburgh, Pa.; Century City, Los Angeles, Cal.; East
Lake Apartments, Grand Rapids, Mich.; Golden Gateway, San Francisco, Cal.; Housing Corp. of America,
Miami, Fla.; Kips Bay Plaza, New York, N.Y.; Lincoln
Towers, New York, N.Y.; Park West Village, New
York, N.Y.; Society Hill, Philadelphia, Pa.; United
Nations Plaza, New York, N.Y.; Washington Plaza,
Pittsburgh, Pa.; Washington Plaza, Seattle, Wash.

APPLIED DEVICES CORPORATION
112 14th Avenue
College Point, New York 11356
(212) 445–4200

MAJOR PRODUCTS:

Inertial guidance and radar systems, computers, commercial photographic equipment

FINANCIAL DATA:

	$ Millions	1969	1968	1967
Net Sales		26.8	14.8	13.6
Net Income		.13	.08	.008
Yr End Mkt Value		15.8		

ANTI-PERSONNEL CONTRACTS:

[Contracts are held by Muncie Gear Works, a subsidiary of Applied Devices]

6/12/68—$10.8 million for fin and nozzle assemblies of 2.75 inch rockets

10/69—$5.2 million for fin and nozzle assemblies of 2.75 inch rockets

OFFICERS AND DIRECTORS:

President: David B. Learner

OUTSIDE DIRECTORS:

Carl M. Mueller: Partner, Loeb, Rhodes & Co.
Daniel A. Porco: Chairman, Oxford Electric Corp.

(Applied Devices Corporation, continued)
Immanuel Kohn
Dr. Eugene B. Kunecci
James Bayles

ANNUAL MEETING:

The annual meeting is held during February in College Point, New York.

PLANTS AND FACILITIES:

Muncie Gear Works, a subsidiary of Applied Devices, produces anti-personnel weapons at its plant in Muncie, Indiana.

Applied Devices leases a plant in College Point, Queens, New York.

On March 18, 1970, the company announced purchase of University Science Center, Inc., of Pittsburgh, Pa. University Science Center serves as a channel for the transfer of technology and learning from research institutions to private and public users.

ARMCO STEEL CORPORATION
703 Curtis Street
Middletown, Ohio 45042
(513) 425–6541

MAJOR PRODUCTS:

Basic steel, oil drilling machinery, leasing operations, truck-mounted campers, snowmobiles, loudspeaker cones, suitcase shells

FINANCIAL DATA:

$ Millions	1969	1968	1967
Net Sales	1565.5	1477.7	1251.7
Net Income	95.7	95.0	70.7
P/E Ratio	11–8	10–8	12–10

ANTI-PERSONNEL CONTRACTS:

[Contracts held by HITCO, a subsidiary of Armco Steel]

FY 68—$10.6 million for fin and nozzle assemblies for 2.75 inch rockets

10/69—$5.1 million for fin and nozzle assemblies for 2.75 inch rockets

[Contracts held by F. T. S. Corp., a subsidiary of HITCO]

$1.7 million for fin and nozzle assemblies for 2.75 inch rockets

(Armco Steel Corporation, continued)
OFFICERS AND DIRECTORS:

Chairman: Logan T. Johnson, Middletown, Ohio (Director: Cincinnati Gas and Electric Co., Standard Oil Co. of Indiana; Trustee: Miami University, Carnegie-Mellon University)
President: C. William Verity, Jr.

OUTSIDE DIRECTORS:

John C. Denton: President, Chemplex Co.

James C. Donnell II: President, Marathon Oil Co.

Herbert J. Frensley: President, Brown and Root, Inc.

Philip O. Geier, Jr.: President, Cincinnati Milling Machine Co.

Joseph B. Hall: Chairman, Selective Insurance Co.

R. Stanley Laing: President, National Cash Register Co.

George P. MacNichol, Jr.

John A. Mayer: Chairman, Mellon National Bank and Trust Co.; Vice-President, General Motors Corp.

T. Spencer Shore: Chairman of the Executive Committee, Eagle-Picher Co.

Edwin J. Thomas: Chairman of Executive Committee, Goodyear Tire and Rubber Co.

ANNUAL MEETING:

The annual meeting of shareholders is held during April in Middletown, Ohio.

PLANT SITES:

Armco maintains steel plants in Middletown and

(Armco Steel Corporation, continued)
Zanesville, Ohio; Ashland, Kentucky; Houston and Dallas, Texas; Kansas City, Missouri; New Orleans, Louisiana; Omaha, Nebraska; Ambridge and Butler, Pennsylvania; Baltimore, Maryland and Sand Springs, Oklahoma.

National Supply Division operates drilling machinery plants in Torrance and Los Nietos, California; Gainesville and Houston, Texas.

HITCO, acquired by Armco Steel in December, 1969, operates plants in Gardena, Santa Ana, Placentia, Huntington Park, Cudahy and Stockton, California; Atlanta, Georgia; Auburn and Marysville, Washington; Denver, Colorado and Lakeville, Minnesota.

F. T. S., a subsidiary of HITCO, makes anti-personnel weapons at its plant in Denver, Colorado.

AVCO CORPORATION
750 Third Avenue
New York, New York 10017
(212) 986–5600

MAJOR PRODUCTS:

Broadcasting, movie production, insurance and loaning services, electronic and aeronautical components, assembly-line houses.

CONSUMER BRANDS:

Avco Delta, Seaboard loaning services, *Paul Revere* insurance and mutual funds, *Avco* savings and loan, *Carte Blanche* credit services, *Avco Embassy* movies and records, *Grand Lodge* mobile homes

FINANCIAL DATA:

$ Millions	1969*	1968
Net Sales	898.1	939.6
Net Income	51.4	57.0
Yr End Mkt Value	285.0	

ANTI-PERSONNEL CONTRACTS:

FY 68—$2.0 million for M423 impact point detonating fuses for 2.75 inch rockets

10/69—$1.3 million for M423 impact point detonating fuses for 2.75 inch rockets

* Avco's annual accounting period ends on November 30 of each calendar year.

(Avco Corporation, continued)
1/70—$1.3 million for M423 impact point detonating
fuses for 2.75 inch rockets

OFFICERS AND DIRECTORS:

Chairman: Kendrick R. Wilson, S. Norwalk, Conn.
(Director: Avon Products, Dayco Corp., Central &
Southwest Corp., Dry Dock Savings Bank, Atlantic
Richfield)
President: James R. Kerr, La Jolla, Cal.
(Director: Connecticut National Bank, Lehman
Corp., Republic Steel, Thiokol Chemical Corp.;
Chairman of the Board of Advisors: Merrimack
College; Trustee: Sacred Heart University)

OUTSIDE DIRECTORS:

George E. Allen: President, Allen Oil Co.

G. Keith Funston: Chairman, Olin Corp.

T. Keith Glennan: Vice-President, Paul Revere Life
Insurance Co.

Francis Harrington: Vice-President, Paul Revere Life
Insurance Co.

Edward Hodgkins: Vice-President, Paul Revere Life
Insurance Co.

Frederick W. P. Jones: Professor at the School of
Business Administration, University of Western
Ontario

Herman Kahn: Partner, Lehman Brothers

John McDougald: Vice-President, Taylor McDougald
Co.

(Avco Corporation, continued)
ANNUAL MEETING:

The annual meeting is customarily held during April in New York City.

PLANTS AND FACILITIES:
Ordnance Division plants are located in Richmond, Indiana. Other plants are located in Nashville, Tennessee; Westboro, Boston, Everett, Haverhill, Wilmington, Lowell and Worcester, Massachusetts; Torrance, California; Washington, D.C.; Glasgow, Montana; San Antonio, Texas; Cincinnati and Coldwater, Ohio; Huntsville, Alabama; Tulsa, Oklahoma; Stratford, Connecticut; Charleston, South Carolina; Williamsport, Pennsylvania; Fort Dodge, Iowa; Baltimore, Maryland and Franklin Park, Illinois.

Paul Revere Life Insurance Co. and Paul Revere Courier Funds, Inc., Avco subsidiaries, are located in Worcester, Massachusetts.

Avco Savings and Loan owns the Coastline Mortgage Corp., Ventura, California.

Carte Blanche Corp., a subsidiary of Avco Corp., owns the Cartan Travel Bureau, Chicago, Illinois.

Avco Broadcasting Corp., located in Cincinnati, Ohio, owns the following television stations: WLWT, Cincinnati, Ohio; WLWC, Columbus, Ohio; WLWD, Dayton, Ohio; WLWI, Indianapolis, Indiana and WOAI, San Antonio, Texas; and the following radio stations: WLW, Cincinnati, Ohio; WOAI, San Antonio, Texas; WWDC, Washington, D.C.; KYA and

(Avco Corporation, continued)
KOIT (FM), San Francisco, California and WRTH, Wood River, Illinois.

Avco Embassy Pictures Corp. is headquartered in New York City.

Avco Financial Services, the product of the proposed consolidation of Avco Delta Finance and Seaboard Finance, will be located in a new facility at Newport Beach, California.

CORPORATE NEWS:

"Early in 1969, Avco Embassy acquired Friwafft Productions from Mike Nichols. Mr. Nichols, who directed 'The Graduate,' has contracted to direct two more pictures, the first of which will be based on a script by Jules Feiffer . . .

"As examples of active response to community needs, personnel at Avco Broadcasting radio and TV stations accomplished the following last year:

—Organized a national panel of disc jockeys to meet at the White House to discuss the mis-use of drugs

—Raised and distributed over $300,000 among approximately 100 hospitals to make hospital stays happier for little children

—Raised $50,000 in one day so a home for teen-age delinquents could continue to operate." *1969 Annual Report,* p. 26

D. H. BALDWIN COMPANY
1801 Gilbert Avenue
Cincinnati, Ohio 44109
(513) 621-4300

MAJOR PRODUCTS:

Pianos, organs, guitars, encoders for the military

CONSUMER BRANDS AND SERVICES:

Baldwin, Gretsch musical instruments; *Central Bank and Trust Co., Empire Savings,* Denver, Colorado

FINANCIAL DATA:

	$ Millions	1969	1968	1967
Net Sales		56.1	61.4	58.7
Net Income		4.5	3.7	2.2
Yr End Mkt Value		55.4		

ANTI-PERSONNEL CONTRACTS:

[Contracts are held by Baldwin Electronics Division]
$3.1 million for loading, assembling and packing of 2.75 inch rocket motors
12/69—$1.7 million contract modification on above contract

OFFICERS AND DIRECTORS:

Chairman: Lucien Wulsin, Cincinnati, Ohio
President: Morley P. Thompson, Cincinnati, Ohio
(Director: Empire Savings and Loan, Hyde Park

(D. H. Baldwin Company, continued)
Savings and Loan, Central Bank and Trust Co.,
Midland Guardian Co.)

OUTSIDE DIRECTORS:

William M. Hickey: President/Director, The United
Corp.
L. H. Kyte: Partner, Kyte, Conlin, Wulsin & Vogeler
W. A. Mitchell: Former Chairman, Central Trust Co.
Robert Fanning: Former Manager, Chicago Division
—D. H. Baldwin Co.
Fred Gretsch, Jr.: President/Director, Fred Gretsch
Co.
Gordon Adamson

ANNUAL MEETING:

The annual meeting is held during April at the corporate offices in Cincinnati.

PLANTS AND SERVICES:

D. H. Baldwin maintains plants in Booneville, Cam-
den, Conway, DeQueen, Fayetteville and Little Rock,
Ark.; Greenwood, Miss.; and Cincinnati, Ohio.
The Baldwin Electronic plant in Little Rock, Ark.
produces anti-personnel weapons.
D. H. Baldwin owns the Central Bank and Trust Com-
pany and Empire Savings & Loan Assn. in Denver,
Colorado.

BEECH AIRCRAFT
9709 East Central Avenue
Wichita, Kansas
(316) 685–6211

MAJOR PRODUCTS:

Commercial and military aircraft

CONSUMER BRANDS:

Beech airplanes

FINANCIAL DATA:

$ Millions	fy1969	1968	1967
Net Sales	187.3	184.4	174.1
Net Income	2.0	7.8	9.0
P/E Ratio	97–40	27–14	17–9
Yr End Mkt Value	32.5		

ANTI-PERSONNEL CONTRACTS:

SUU 7C/A dispensers and M468 shipping containers:
8/67–$995,000

1/68–$1.6 million

7/68–$940,500 initial letter contract for SUU–7C/A
   dispensers and containers

10/68–$2.1 million modification on 7/68 contract

OFFICERS AND DIRECTORS:

Chairman: O. A. Beech, Wichita, Kansas
   (Director: Fourth National Bank, Wichita)

(Beech Aircraft, continued)
President: Frank E. Hedrick
  (Vice President/Director: Cowie Electric Co.;
  Director: Southwest Grease & Oil Co.)

OUTSIDE DIRECTORS:

A. R. Bell
Chandler Hovery, Jr.

ANNUAL MEETING:

The stockholders' meeting is customarily held in
Wichita during December.

PLANTS:

Beech maintains manufacturing plants in Wichita,
Salina and Liberal, Kansas and Boulder, Colorado.
Salina, Liberal and Boulder all manufacture military
hardware.

BRUNSWICK CORPORATION
69 West Washington Street
Chicago, Illinois 60602
(312) 341–7000

MAJOR PRODUCTS:
Medical supplies, bowling products, yachts, aerospace and airplane components

CONSUMER BRANDS:

Burke, Hugh Acton furniture; *Mac Gregor, Zebco* and *Brunswick* sports equipment; *Flagship, Owens* yachts; *Mercury* marine products, snowmobiles; *Quicksilver* marine products; *Blizzard* skis and accessories; *Anba* ski clothing; *San Marco* ski boots

FINANCIAL DATA:

$ Millions	1969	1968	1967
Net Sales	449.6	421.6	379.1
Net Income	14.5	12.6	6.1
P/E Ratio	32–18	30–18	44–21
Yr End Mkt Value	334.7		

ANTI-PERSONNEL CONTRACTS:

$2.0 million for SUU 7C/A dispensers
$1.2 million for XM200 launchers for 2.75 inch rockets (2/70)

OFFICERS AND DIRECTORS:

Chairman: B. Edward Bensinger, Highland Park,

(Brunswick Corporation, continued)

Illinois (Trustee: University of Chicago; Member of Board: Northwestern University; Director: American National Bank & Trust Co., Inland Life Insurance Co.)

President: John Hanigan, Glencoe, Illinois

OUTSIDE DIRECTORS:

John T. Rettaliata: President, Illinois Institute of Technology

Robert Straus: Chairman, American National Bank & Trust Co.

Harold Szold: Partner, Lehman Bros.

R. F. Bensinger: Retired Chairman, Brunswick Corp.

Pierre Rinfret: Chairman, Lionel D. Edie Co.

Robert Sabin: President/Director, Ekco Products Co.

L. A. Appley: Chairman, American Management Assn.

J. G. Sevcik: President/Director, Burton Dixie Corp.

Walter Heymann: Director, First National Bank of Chicago

ANNUAL MEETING:

The annual meeting is customarily held during April in Chicago.

PLANTS:

Brunswick maintains plants at Tulsa, Okla.; Covington and Albany, Georgia; Marion, Virginia; Kalamazoo and Muskegon, Michigan; Needham and Ware, Mass.; Norfolk and Lincoln, Neb.; Dallas, Texas; Argyle, N.Y.; Baltimore, Maryland; St. Louis and

(Brunswick Corporation, continued)
Brentwood, Missouri; Cincinnati, Ohio; De Land, Florida; Eminence, Kentucky; Waterbury and Torrington, Conn.; and Cedarburg, Fond du Lac and Oshkosh, Wisc.

BULOVA WATCH CO., INC.
630 Fifth Avenue
New York, New York 10020
(212) 581–0400

MAJOR PRODUCTS:

Watches, clocks, radios, timing devices, electronic and defense products

CONSUMER BRANDS:

Bulova, Accutron, Caravelle, Empress clocks, radios, clock-radios, watches

FINANCIAL DATA:

$ Millions	3/31/69*	1968	1967
Net Sales	148.9	139.8	123.9
Net Income	5.9	4.5	3.9
P/E Ratio	18–9	15–10	13–7
Yr End Mkt Value	198.5		

ANTI-PERSONNEL CONTRACTS:

$1.4 million for M423 impact point detonating fuses
   for 2.75 inch rockets
2/69—$1.2 million modification on above contract
10/69—$2.5 million modification on above contract

OFFICERS AND DIRECTORS:

Chairman: Omar Bradley, Beverly Hills, California

* Bulova's annual accounting period ends on March 31 of each calendar year.

(Bulova Watch Co., Inc. continued)
    (Trustee: Research Analysis Corp.; Director: Metro-Goldwyn-Mayer, Food Fair Stores)
President: Harry B. Henshel, Scarsdale, New York
    (Director: American Management Association)

OUTSIDE DIRECTORS:

R. Clyde Allen: Executive Vice-President and Director, Stewart, Dougall and Associates

Benjamin Dorsey: President and Director, Equity Annuity Life Insurance Co.

Rodney Gott: Chairman and President, American Machine and Foundry Co.

James McCormack: Chairman, Communications Satellite Corp.

John Weinberg: Partner, Goldman Sachs and Co.

ANNUAL MEETING:

The annual meeting is customarily held during July at Bulova Park in Jackson Heights, New York.

PLANTS:

Bulova maintains plants at Flushing, Woodside, South Valley Stream, Sag Harbor and Westbury, New York.

CORPORATE PHILOSOPHY:

"Regarding our defense activities, we would truly welcome for a variety of considerations an end to the hostilities in Vietnam. Though we did experience an unexpected rise in business from this area in 1968–69, any fall-off from this level would most likely be grad-

(Bulova Watch Co., Inc. continued)
ual, as the Armed Forces that Bulova supplies with
ordnance fuzes would certainly want to rebuild presently dwindling stockpiles."

1969 Annual Report, p. 17

"The esoteric-sounding inventory of principal products
of the non-consumer units—fuzes, safe and arming devices, micro-bonders, crystal filters, optical choppers,
tuning fork oscillators, laser beam choppers—seem re-
mote from watch design and manufacture, but they
represent an inhouse technological base whose impact
can be company-wide."

1968 Annual Report, pp. 16–17

"The increasing number of diversified non-defense
projects . . . indicate the trend the company projects.
Commitments to material for Vietnam have thus far
inhibited full-scale development of industrial appli-
cations, but the technology and technical manpower
exist."

1968 Annual Report, p. 17

CCI CORPORATION (Formerly CCI Marquardt Corp.)
4111 S. Darlington
Tulsa, Oklahoma
(918) 622–5903

MAJOR PRODUCTS:

Rocket engines, navigational systems, heavy duty industrial carriers, railroad signals, communications devices, software, water desalinization and waste management research

FINANCIAL DATA:

	$ Millions 4/30/1969*	1968	1967
Net Sales	103.9	112.1	97.8
Net Income	3.7	2.7	4.8
P/E Ratio	22–17		

ANTI-PERSONNEL CONTRACTS:

[Contracts are held by the Marquardt Corp., a division of CCI]

6/68—$3.0 million for fin and nozzle assemblies for 2.75 inch rockets

10/69—$4.9 million for fin and nozzle assemblies for 2.75 inch rockets

* CCI Corporation's annual accounting period ends on April 30 of each calendar year.

(CCI Corporation, continued)

OFFICERS AND DIRECTORS:

Chairman: Robert L. Zeligson, Tulsa, Oklahoma
President: J. B. Montgomery

OUTSIDE DIRECTORS:

Joseph H. Flom: Secretary, Kaysam Corp. of America
Raymond F. Kravis: Consulting Petroleum Engineer
David D. Levy: Securities Analyst, Bare, Sterns and
Co.
B. Allison Gillies: Chairman, Spectral Dynamics Corp.
Alan C. Greenberg: Partner, Bare, Sterns and Co.
T. F. Walkowicz
Harper Woodward

PLANT SITES:

Plants are operated in Huntington Park, Van Nuys and
Pomona, California; Ogden, Utah; Chicago, Illinois
and Irving, Texas.

CESSNA AIRCRAFT
5800 East Pawnee Road
Wichita, Kansas
(316) 685–9111

MAJOR PRODUCTS:

Airplane and airplane parts, hydraulic systems, communication and navigation equipment

CONSUMER BRANDS:

Cessna airplanes

FINANCIAL DATA:

$ Millions	FY 1969	1968	1967
Net Sales	282.3	264.3	213.6
Net Income	15.2	12.8	10.8
P/E Ratio	13–10	17–11	16–12
Yr End Mkt Value	166.6		

ANTI-PERSONNEL CONTRACTS:

10/67—$2.3 million for SUU–7C/A dispensers with containers

1/68—$3.6 million for SUU–7C/A dispensers

7/68—$986,957 initial letter contract for SUU–7C/A

10/68—$1.9 million contract for SUU–7C/A; modifications of this contract have amounted to $5.4 million

$300,000 for XM3 anti-personnel mine dispensers

$35,076 for XM3 anti-personnel mine dispensers

(Cessna Aircraft, continued)

OFFICERS AND DIRECTORS:

Chairman: Dwayne L. Wallace, Wichita, Kansas
(Director: Kansas Gas & Electric, Coleman Co.,
Fourth National Bank in Wichita)

President: Delbert Roskam, Wichita, Kansas
(Director: National Aero Finance Co., Aircraft
Radio Co., Reims Aviation)

OUTSIDE DIRECTORS:

Sheldon Coleman: Chairman/President, Coleman Co.

Ray Dillon: Chairman, J. S. Dillon & Sons Stores

Hugh Quinn: Partner, McDonald, Tinker, Skaer,
Quinn and Harrington

Harding L. Lawrence: President/Chief Executive,
Braniff International

ANNUAL MEETING:

The annual meeting is customarily held during January in Wichita, Kansas.

PLANTS:

Cessna operates plants in Boonton, New Jersey; Dayton, Ohio; Hutchinson and Wichita, Kansas.

CITY INVESTING COMPANY
P.O. Box 777
Tuxedo, New York 10987
(212) 988–8000

MAJOR PRODUCTS:

Holds diversified manufacturing companies, and investment, housing and land development companies

CONSUMER BRANDS:

Roberts tape recorders; *Rheem, Ruud* water heaters

FINANCIAL DATA:

$ Millions	1969*	1968	1967
Net Sales	364.1	207.0	150.7
Net Income	48.1	12.1	6.7
P/E Ratio	20–9	26–9	18–9
Yr End Mkt Value	551.1		

ANTI-PERSONNEL CONTRACTS:

[Contracts held by American Electric, a subsidiary of City Investing (American Electric also produces napalm)]

2/68—$2.6 million for SUU–30B/B "Sadeye" dispensers and containers

10/69—$3.8 million for SUU–30B/B "Sadeye" dispensers and containers

* City Investing's annual accounting period ends on April 30 of each calendar year.

(City Investing Company, continued)

[Contracts held by Hayes-International, a subsidiary of City Investing]

6–12/68—$1.3 million for M151 warheads for 2.75 inch rockets

4/69—$1.2 million modification on above contract

OFFICERS AND DIRECTORS:

Chairman: Robert W. Dowling, New York City (Director: Dowling College, United Artists, New York Airways, Chemway Corp., Hilton International, Waldorf-Astoria Hotel Corp., R. H. Macy, First National City Trust Co., Emigrant Industrial Savings Bank)

President: George T. Scharffenberger, Rolling Hills, California (Chairman: Gateway National Bank; Director: Metro-Goldwyn-Mayer, Moore and Mac-Cormack Co.)

OUTSIDE DIRECTORS:

John R. Dunning: Chairman, Sheer-Korman Associates

James Felt: Planning consultant

Walter D. Fletcher: Partner, Davis, Polk and Wardwell

Leon Forst: Attorney

John L. Gibbons: Former Executive Vice-President, Chairman of the Trust Committee, Chemical Bank of New York

John W. Houser: Consultant, American Express Co.

Lewis F. Jeffers: Chairman, Hayes-International

(City Investing Company, continued)

Roswell Messing, Jr.: President, World Color Press

Lionel I. Pincus: President, E. M. Warburg and Co.

Eben W. Pyne: Senior Vice-President, First National City Bank

Emanuel J. Rousuck: Vice-President, Wildenstein and Company

A. Lightfoot Walker: Former President, Chairman of the Executive Committee, Rheem Manufacturing Company

George H. Walker, Jr.: Partner, G. H. Walker and Co.

Ernest Wolff: Partner, Winter, Wolff and Co.

ANNUAL MEETING:

The annual meeting is customarily held during October in New York City.

PLANT SITES AND FACILITIES:

Motel 6, Inc., a City Investing subsidiary, operates a chain of over 600 motels.

Rheem Manufacturing Co., a City Investing subsidiary, produces *Roberts* tape recorders. They maintain 18 plants at various locations in the country.

Main offices of American Electric, a City Investing subsidiary, are in La Mirada, California.

Hayes-International, a City Investing subsidiary, produces anti-personnel weapons at its plant in Birmingham, Alabama. Other Hayes-International plants are located in Dothan and Huntsville, Alabama; Elizabeth

(City Investing Company, continued)
City, North Carolina and Hondo, Texas. City Investing owns World Color Press, Inc., one of the world's
largest printers of magazines. Subsidiaries of WCP
are Chemical Plate, Inc. & Post Photo Engraving
Corp.

City Investing also owns 54% of the stock of Guerdon
Industries, one of the nation's largest producers of
mobile homes. City Investing is reportedly attempting
a take-over. Guerdon maintains plants in Brighton,
Michigan; Newton, Kansas; Chambersburg, Pennsyl-
vania; Lake City, Florida; Boise, Idaho and Corona,
California. They market trailers under the following
trade names: *Great Lakes, Van Dyke, Cranbrook,*
Belmont, Vagabond, Embassy, Viceroy, Diplomat,
Magnolia, Armor, Aire-Line and *Statler Richmond.*

E. I. DU PONT DE NEMOURS AND CO.
1007 Market Street
Wilmington, Delaware
(302) 774–1000

MAJOR PRODUCTS:

Explosives, chemicals, textiles, rubber and plastics, petroleum refining, machinery, food products, fibers (duPont is the world's largest producer of fibers. They make Acele, Dacron polyester, Lycra spandex, Antron, Cantrece, Qiana, Nomex, Orlon and Teflon)

CONSUMER BRANDS:

duPont paints; *Zerone, Zerex* and *Telar* anti-freezes

FINANCIAL DATA:

$ Millions	1969	1968	1967
Net Sales	3655.3	3481.2	3102.0
Net Income	356.2	371.9	313.9
P/E Ratio	23–14	23–19	28–22

ANTI-PERSONNEL CONTRACTS:

11/67—$97,200 for development of XM45E1 gravel mines

$1.1 million for production of XM45E1 gravel mines

OFFICERS AND DIRECTORS:

Chairman: L. duPont Copeland (VP: Christiana Se-

(E. I. duPont de Nemours and Co., continued)
 curities; Director: Chemical Bank, Wilmington
 Trust Co.)

President: Charles B. McCoy, Wilmington, Delaware
 (Director: First National City Bank, Wilmington
 Trust Co., Diamond State Telephone Co.)

OUTSIDE DIRECTORS:

W. J. Beadle

W. Samuel Carpenter III

C. A. Cary

J. E. Crane

Emile F. duPont

H. B. duPont: Former Vice-President, E. I. duPont
 de Nemours

George P. Edwards: Chairman, Wilmington Trust Co.

Robert L. Hershey: Former Vice-President, E. I. du-
 Pont de Nemours

William Winder Laird

Bernard Peyton

Robert L. Richards: Vice-President, Norton Simon
 and Co.

Crawford H. Greenawalt

Hugh R. Sharp, Jr.

ANNUAL MEETING:

The annual meeting of shareholders is held during
April in Wilmington, Delaware.

PLANT SITES:

duPont operates 93 plants in 30 states.

They operate a government-owned plant for the pro-

(E. I. duPont de Nemours and Co., continued)
duction of nuclear materials on the Savannah River,
under contract with the Atomic Energy Commission.
duPont owns 60% of the common stock and 90% of
the preferred stock of Remington Arms Co. of Bridgeport, Connecticut. The company manufactures rifles,
sporting powder, ammunition, chain saws and other
power tools.

FAIRCHILD CAMERA
AND INSTRUMENT CORPORATION
464 Ellis Street
Mountain View, California 94040
(415) 962–5011

MAJOR PRODUCTS:

Electron tubes, graphic electronic equipment, semi-conductors, systems for aerospace reconnaissance

CONSUMER BRANDS:

Dumont electron tubes; *Fairchild* aerial cameras

FINANCIAL DATA:

$ Millions	1969	1968	1967
Net Sales	250.7	198.5	196.9
Net Income	1.0	.6	–7.5
P/E Ratio	150+		
Yr End Mkt Value	404.4		

ANTI-PERSONNEL CONTRACTS:

6 to 12/68–$3.1 million for M429 proximity fuses for 2.75 inch rockets

OFFICERS AND DIRECTORS:

Chairman: Sherman Fairchild, Huntington, Long Island, N.Y. (Chairman: Fairchild Hiller Corp., Dynar Corp.; Owner: Fairchild Recording Equip-

(Fairchild Camera & Instrument Corp., continued)
  ment Corp.; Director: IBM, Giannini Controls
  Corp.)
President: G. L. Hogan

OUTSIDE DIRECTORS:

William Franklin
Walter Burke: Financial Advisor to Sherman Fairchild
Joseph B. Wharton, Jr.: President, Wealdon Co.
Roswell Gilpatric: Partner, Cravath, Swaine & Moore
William Stenson: Executive Vice-President, Bank of
  New York

ANNUAL MEETING:

The annual meeting is held during May in Mountain
View, California.

PLANTS:

Plants are located in Syosset, Copiague, Woodbury,
Hicksville, Farmingdale, Commack, Amsterdam and
Plainview, N.Y.; Palo Alto, Mountain View, San Ra-
fael, El Cajon, Los Angeles and El Segundo, Cal.;
Clifton and Paramus, N.J.; Shiprock, N.M.; Joplin,
Mo.; and South Portland, Me.

FMC CORPORATION
1105 Coleman
San Jose, California 95110
(408) 289–0111

MAJOR PRODUCTS:

Chemicals, ferrous castings, pumps, packaging machinery, canning and frozen food equipment, tractors, auto pollution control equipment, military equipment

CONSUMER BRANDS:

Bolens tractors, lawnmowers and snowmobiles; *Link Belt* construction equipment; *Furatan* insecticide; *Tandex* weed killer; *CDB–63* swimming pool sanitizer

FINANCIAL DATA:

	$ Millions	1969	1968	1967
Net Sales		1409.3	1376.2	1313.0
Net Income		67.3	75.2	60.8
P/E Ratio		19–10	19–14	21–16

ANTI-PERSONNEL CONTRACTS:

1/67—$498,960 for development of testing equipment for the XM27 anti-personnel mine

FY 68—$450,000 to develop semi-automatic system to produce XM41E1 anti-personnel mines; $772,791 for design and development of XM4 anti-personnel mine dispenser; $650,124 for assemblies of XM-594E1 gravel mine

(FMC Corporation, continued)
OFFICERS AND DIRECTORS:

Chairman: James M. Hait, San Jose, California (Director: Interspace Corporation, Wells Fargo Bank, Pacific Gas and Electric Co., Varian Associates, Georgia-Pacific Corporation)

President: Jack M. Pope, San Jose, California (Director: Crocker Citizens National Bank, Crocker National Corporation)

OUTSIDE DIRECTORS:

Robert C. Becherer: Chairman, Link-Belt Ltd. (Division of FMC)

Harlan B. Collins: President, Link-Belt Ltd. (Division of FMC)

Paul L. Davies, Sr.: Senior Partner, Lehman Brothers; Senior Partner FMC, Financial Chairman FMC

Paul L. Davies, Jr.: Partner, Pillsbury, Madison and Sutro

Russell Giffen: President, Giffen Inc.

Albert H. Gordon: Chairman, Kidder, Peabody and Co., Inc.

William R. Hewlett: President and Chief Executive Officer, Hewlett-Packard Co.

George Lund: Former Vice-President, Standard Oil of California

Carl F. Prutton: Former Executive Vice-President, FMC

William N. Williams: Consultant, FMC; Former Executive Vice-President, FMC

(FMC Corporation, continued)

ANNUAL MEETING:

The annual meeting is held during April.

PLANTS:

Defense plants are located in South Charleston, West Virginia; San Jose and Santa Clara, California; and Minneapolis, Minnesota.

Gunderson Brothers Engineering Corporation, a subsidiary of FMC, operates a truck sales and service agency in Eugene, Oregon.

Other FMC plants are in Michigan, Wisconsin, Indiana, Florida, Louisiana, Illinois, Ohio, Oregon, Maryland, Georgia, Pennsylvania, Texas, California, Washington, Iowa, New Hampshire, Virginia, Arizona, Alabama, New Jersey, New York, Massachusetts, Mississippi, Kansas, Idaho, Wyoming, West Virginia, Nevada and Delaware.

GENERAL MOTORS
3044 West Grand Boulevard
Detroit, Michigan 48202
(313) 556–5000

MAJOR PRODUCTS:

Produces approximately 50% of all cars, trucks and buses in the United States. A. C. Division produces navigation and control systems and components, spark plugs and other automotive accessories.

CONSUMER BRANDS:

Chevrolet, Cadillac, Buick, Oldsmobile, Pontiac automobiles; *GMC* trucks and buses; *AC* spark plugs and accessories; *Delco, Frigidaire* appliances

FINANCIAL DATA:

$ Millions	1969	1968	1967
Net Sales	24,295.1	22,755.4	20,026.3
Net Income	1,710.7	1,731.9	1,627.3
P/E Ratio	14–11	15–12	16–12
Yr End Mkt Value	19,689.8		

ANTI-PERSONNEL CONTRACTS:

[Contracts are held by A. C. Electronics, a division of General Motors]

9/68–$267,787 for M158E1 2.75 inch rocket launchers
10/68–$173,491 for launchers and wiring conduit assemblies

(General Motors, continued)
12/68—$267,375 for 2.75 inch rocket launchers
4/69—$168,145 for XM158 2.75 inch rocket launchers
$269,062 for M158A1 2.75 inch rocket launchers
$1.0 million for XM200 2.75 inch rocket launchers

OFFICERS AND DIRECTORS:

Chairman: James Roche, Bloomfield Hills, Michigan
President: Edward N. Cole, Bloomfield Hills, Michigan (Member of the Business Executive Council of the Michigan State University School of Business Administration)

OUTSIDE DIRECTORS:

Eugene N. Beesely: President and Director, Eli Lilly and Co.

Lloyd D. Brace: Chairman and Director, Bank of Boston International

Albert Bradley: Former Chairman, General Motors

Harlee Branch, Jr.: President, Southern Co.

John T. Connor: President, Allied Chemical Co.

Frederic G. Donnor: Chairman, The Sloan Foundation

John F. Gordon: Former President, General Motors

James R. Killian, Jr.: Chairman, Massachusetts Institute of Technology

John A. Mayer

J. Wesley McAfee: Chairman, Union Electric Co.

W. Earle McLaughlin: Chairman and President, Royal Bank of Canada

(General Motors, continued)

Richard K. Mellon: President and Director, T. Mellon and Sons

Howard J. Morgens: President and Director, Proctor and Gamble

Charles S. Mott: Former Vice-President, General Motors; Former Chairman, U. S. Sugar; Chairman and Treasurer, C. S. Mott Foundation

Thomas L. Perkins: Counsel, Perkins, Daniels and McCormack

Albert L. Williams: Former President, International Business Machines

Gerald A. Sivage: President, Marshall Field and Co.

ANNUAL MEETING:

The annual meeting is held during May in Detroit.

PLANT SITES:

Anti-personnel weapons are produced by the A. C. Electronics Division, Huntsville, Alabama.

GENERAL TIME CORPORATION*
High Ridge Park
Stamford, Connecticut
(203) 322–7611

MAJOR PRODUCTS:

Clocks, watches, timing devices, electric motors

CONSUMER BRANDS:

LaSalle, Westclox, Big Ben, Baby Ben, Seth Thomas watches and clocks; *Magnatrol, Time Mist, Acrotimer, Incremag* timing devices

---

* Talley Industries gained control of General Time and installed a new management team last year. The new directors proposed the merger of General Time into Talley and got the approval of the stockholders. Acting in favor of a minority group of General Time shareholders, however, the Securities and Exchange Commission ruled in January, 1970, that the terms of the merger were unfair, and outlined amendments to be made before approval. They approved a revised proposal on February 11, 1970, and the final vote of the shareholders of both companies has been set for May 14, 1970.

Talley Industries, of Mesa, Arizona, manufactures aircraft escape systems, plastic automobile parts, snow blowers, ladies knitted sportswear, outboard motors and gas starter cartridges. Sales to the government accounted for 80% of revenues in fiscal year 1967–68.

Franz G. Talley is President of Talley Industries. The company maintains plants in Maricopa, Arizona and Lindenhurst, New York.

(General Time Corporation, continued)

FINANCIAL DATA:

$ Millions	1969	1968	1967
Net Sales	160.1	143.5	129.5
Net Income	6.5	5.5	3.8
P/E Ratio		23–11	14–8
Yr End Mkt Value	68.3		

ANTI-PERSONNEL CONTRACTS:

FY 68—$1.7 million for M423 impact point detonating fuses for 2.75 inch rockets
$1.7 million for M427 impact mechanical point detonating fuses for 2.75 inch rockets

6/69—$2.9 million for Mk339 time fuses for the Rockeye II

10/69—$2.9 million for metal parts for 2.75 inch rocket point detonating fuses

11/69—$1.2 million for Rockeye II mechanical time fuses

$3.2 million for XM571E1 fuses for 90mm Beehive projectiles

$250,000 for XM592E1 fuses for anti-personnel projectiles

OFFICERS AND DIRECTORS:

Chairman: Wesley A. Stanger, Cranford, N.J. (Chairman: Gibraltar Growth Fund; Partner: Riter and Co.; Director: Madison Fund, Pacific Drug Distributors, American–South African Investment Co., Ltd., Eurofund International)

President: Gerald E. Hirt

(General Time Corporation, continued)

Outside Directors:

Mark W. Lowell

Louis C. Lustenberger: Former President, Chairman of the Executive Committee and Director, W. T. Grant Co.

William M. Robbins: Former President, General Foods Corp.

Robert J. Koenig: President, Cerro Corp.

William H. Osborne, Jr.

William T. Taylor: Former Chairman, Chairman of the Executive Committee, A. C. F. Industries

Walter H. Wheeler, Jr.: Chairman, Pitney-Bowes

Lawrence H. Appley, Jr.: Chairman, American Management Association

Plants:

General Time operates plants in Athens, Georgia; Emigsville, Pennsylvania; La Salle, Rolling Hills and Skokie, Illinois; Stamford and Thomaston, Connecticut.

GENERAL TIRE AND RUBBER COMPANY
1708 Englewood Avenue
Akron, Ohio 44309
(216) 798–3000

MAJOR PRODUCTS:

Tires and tubes, chemicals and plastics, rubber and metal products, rocket components and propellants

CONSUMER BRANDS AND SERVICES:

Pennsylvania tennis equipment, *General* tires, *RKO* theatres and radio stations

FINANCIAL DATA:

$ Millions	1969	1968	1967
Net Sales	1087.8	1039.1	954.5
Net Income	35.1	43.3	32.1
P/E Ratio	17–8	15–9	26–16
Yr End Mkt Value	319.7		

ANTI-PERSONNEL CONTRACTS:

[Contracts held by General Tire and Rubber Chemicals/Plastics Division]
1/69—$789,118 for metal parts for M18 and M18A1 Claymore anti-personnel mines

[Contracts held by Aerojet General, a subsidiary of General Tire and Rubber]
Downey, California Plant
FY 64—$3.5 million for SUU–14A/A dispensers

(General Tire and Rubber Company, continued)

FY 64—Engineering study of release of self-dispersing
munitions from high speed airborne vehicles

6/66—$2.3 million for SUU–30/B Sadeye dispensers

1/67—$3.2 million for Sadeye cluster bombs

1/68—$558,000 letter contract for SUU–30B/B Sadeye
dispensers and CNU–105E containers

4/68—$224,750 for Research and Development of
Phase I of XM56 mine dispenser

8/68—$1.2 million initial letter contract for cluster
bomb dispensers

11/68—$1.2 million modification on above contract

1/69—$1.2 million for M151 warheads for 2.75 inch
rockets

Fullerton, California Plant

8/69—$878,977 for CBU–38/A munition dispenser
training items and data

[Contracts held by Batesville Manufacturing Company, a subsidiary of Aerojet General]

FY 68—$1.3 million for SUU–30A/B Sadeye cluster
bomb dispensers

FY 68—$113,654 for M26 anti-personnel mine metal
parts; $2.5 million increment to a $5.0 million contract for BLU–24/B and BLU–66/B metal parts

1/68—$1.68 million letter contract for SUU–30B/B
Sadeye dispensers and containers, and data

4/68—$1.3 million for SUU–30A/B Sadeye dispensers
with CNU–105E containers

(General Tire and Rubber Company, continued)

8/68—$2.0 million increment to a $5.0 million fixed-price contract for CBU–30/A aircraft dispenser and bomb

9/68—$2.1 million increment to a $5.1 million contract for cluster bomb dispensers

11/68—$1.1 million increment to an $8.6 million definitive fixed-price contract for BLU–66/B fragmentation bombs

4/69—$4.8 million definitive fixed-price contract for BLU–24/B and BLU–66/B fragmentation bombs

5/69—two dispenser/container awards totaling $6.6 million

10/69—$2.2 million for SUU–30 dispensers

OFFICERS AND DIRECTORS:

Chairman: Thomas O'Neil, Greenwich, Connecticut (Director: Companion Life Insurance Co., Horn and Hardart)

President: M. G. O'Neil, Akron, Ohio (Director: First National Bank of Akron, Houdaille Industries, Pneumo Dynamics)

OUTSIDE DIRECTORS:

F. W. Knowlton

D. A. Kimball: Ex-Secretary of the Navy; Chairman/President, Aerojet General

O. G. Vinnedge

W. E. Zisch: Vice-Chairman, Aerojet General

J. E. Powers

(General Tire and Rubber Company, continued)

ANNUAL MEETING:

The annual meeting is held during March at the company's offices in Akron, Ohio.

PLANTS AND FACILITIES:

The Tire Division maintains plants in Akron, Bryan and Cuyahoga Falls, Ohio; Barnesville and Macon, Georgia; Charlotte, North Carolina; City of Industry, California; Mayfield, Kentucky and Waco, Texas.

The Chemical/Plastics Division maintains plants in Ashtabula, Mogadore, Newcomerstown and Toledo, Ohio; Columbus, Mississippi; Jeanette, Pennsylvania; Lawrence, Massachusetts; Marion, Indiana; Odessa, Texas and Orange, California.

Industrial Products has headquarters in Wabash, Indiana and plants in Evansville, Logansport and Peru, Indiana, and Fort Smith, Arkansas.

RKO General, Inc., a subsidiary of General Tire and Rubber, has headquarters in New York City. They own the following TV stations: WOR, New York; KHJ, Los Angeles; WNAC, Boston; WHBQ, Memphis, Tennessee; CKLW, Windsor, Ontario and WHCT, Hartford, Connecticut. They own the following radio stations: WOR, New York; KHJ, Los Angeles; WROR, Boston; WHBQ, Memphis; CKLW, Windsor, Ontario; KFRC and KFMA, San Francisco and WGMS, Washington, D.C.

(General Tire and Rubber Company, continued)
RKO General also owns Video Independent Theatres, Inc., of Oklahoma City, which operates a chain of 127 motion picture theaters; Frontier Airlines of Denver, Colorado; The Equinox House of Manchester, Vermont and The Christie Inn of Londonberry, Vermont.

Aerojet General Corp., a subsidiary of General Tire and Rubber Co., has plants in Azusa, Chino, El Monte, Sacramento, Downey and Fullerton, California; Frederick, Maryland and Homestead, Florida.

Subsidiaries of Aerojet General are Watts Manufacturing Co. of Compton, California and Batesville Manufacturing Co. of Batesville and Camden, Arkansas.

HAMILTON WATCH, INC.
Columbia Avenue
Lancaster, Pennsylvania 17604
(717) 394-7161

MAJOR PRODUCTS:

Watches, clocks, timing devices, flatware, defense
products

CONSUMER BRANDS AND SERVICES:

Vantage, Hamilton, Buren timepieces; *Wallace and
Tuttle* silver products
Semca subsidiary produces *Semca, Phinney-Walker*
and *Forestville* clocks

FINANCIAL DATA:

$ Millions	1/30/70*	1969	1968
Net Sales	89.0	79.0	68.4
Net Income	2.0	2.3	1.9
P/E Ratio	31–15	31–16	22–17
Yr End Mkt Value	29.7		

ANTI-PERSONNEL CONTRACTS:

$1.2 million for M423 fuse parts for 2.75 inch rockets
$1.1 million for XM592E1 fuses for anti-personnel
   projectiles

* Hamilton's annual accounting period ends on January 31
of each calendar year.

(Hamilton Watch, Inc., continued)

OFFICERS AND DIRECTORS:

Chairman: Arthur B. Sinkler, Millersville, Pennsylvania (Director: Farmer's Bank and Trust Co., Bush Universal)

President: Richard J. Blakinger, Lancaster, Pennsylvania

OUTSIDE DIRECTORS:

John F. McGlinn

H. J. Caster: President, Caster Realty Corp.; Director: Bush Universal, Inc.

W. E. Overley: President, G. H. Delp Co.; Director, Bush Universal, Inc.

Jacob Hain: Chairman, Bush Universal, Inc.

J. C. Hilly: Vice-Chairman, Bush Universal, Inc.

Ralph Holt, Jr.: Vice-President and Treasurer, Holt Hosiery Mills; Director, Bush Universal, Inc.

Paul F. Mickey: Partner, Steptoe and Johnson

Clarence Ritter: President, First National Bank of Shoemakersville, Pa.; Director, Bush Universal, Inc.

Morris Shilensky: Partner, Hays, St. John, Abramson and Heilbron; Director, Bush Universal, Inc.

Edward Hain: Secretary-Treasurer, Bush Universal, Inc.

Donald Mathews: President, Bush Universal, Inc.

R. A. Fulton

ANNUAL MEETING:

The annual meeting is held during May in Lancaster, Pennsylvania.

(Hamilton Watch, Inc., continued)

PLANTS:

Hamilton maintains plants in E. Petersburg and Lancaster, Pa.; Long Island City, N.Y. and Wallingford, Conn.
Semca Clock Co. and Forestville Clock Co., wholly-owned subsidiaries, operate plants in Long Island City, N.Y.

CORPORATE PHILOSOPHY:

"The military products division was successful on high volume production contracts for military fuses after experiencing setbacks in 1967. Hamilton became the leader in the production of one of these fuses as indicated by production volume, size of production lots and low reject rate. . .

"Realizing the need for diversification within the military products division, a vigorous research and development program was undertaken in 1968 . . . The primary objective in the expanded research and development activity will be to broaden the product line and increase the list of active customers while providing a necessary vehicle for the acquisition of new product contracts." *1968 Annual Report*, p. 10–11.

BUSH UNIVERSAL, INC.:

This company owns over 50% of the stock of Hamilton Watch. On 1/29/70, the two companies announced that their respective directors had authorized the managements to explore ways and means of com-

(Hamilton Watch, Inc., continued)
bining the two concerns. On 6/2/70, Bush and Hamilton announced agreement on a merger plan of the two companies. The merger is subject to the approval of shareholders.

Bush Universal owns some 150 acres of land on the Brooklyn, N.Y., waterfront, on which is erected one of the largest freight terminals in the world. Facilities include 7 steamship piers, 105 industrial buildings, 18 miles of railroad and yard facilities for handling 1000 freight cars.

Universal Terminal and Stevedoring Corp. and Seaboard Stevedoring Corp., subsidiaries of Bush Universal, Inc. provide stevedoring services in New York City and Philadelphia.

HAMMOND CORPORATION
100 Wilmot Road
Deerfield, Illinois 60015
(312) 945–4700

MAJOR PRODUCTS:

Electronic organs, fuses, work and sporting gloves

CONSUMER BRANDS:

Wells Lamont gloves, *Gibbs* auto-tape players, *Hammond* organs, *Everett* and *Cable-Nelson* pianos, *Condor* sound modulators

FINANCIAL DATA:

$ Millions	3/31/69*	1968	1967
Net Sales	90.5	83.6	80.8
Net Income	5.3	4.6	5.2
P/E Ratio	18–9	18–10	18–12
Yr End Mkt Value	51.4		

ANTI-PERSONNEL CONTRACTS:

[Contracts are held by Gibbs Mfg. and Research, a Hammond subsidiary]

$2.0 million for M427 2.75 inch rocket fuse metal parts

6/69–$1.8 million contract modification on above contract

---

* Hammond's annual accounting period ends on March 31 of each calendar year.

(Hammond Corporation, continued)
OFFICERS AND DIRECTORS:

Chairman: Stanley M. Sorenson, Park Ridge, Illinois
   (President: Foundation for Human Ecology)
President: John A. Volkober, Park Ridge, Illinois
   (Director: Everett Piano Co.)

OUTSIDE DIRECTORS:

Corliss D. Anderson: Retired Managing Partner, Duff,
   Anderson & Clark; Retired Chairman, Department
   of Finance, School of Business—Northwestern Uni-
   versity
Gregson L. Barker: President, Uarco, Inc.
Warren C. Horton: Counsel, Horton, Davis, McCaleb
   & Lucas
J. Milton Moon: President, Signode Corp.
Darrell E. Peterson: President, Scott, Foresman & Co.

ANNUAL MEETING:

The annual meeting is customarily held during July
in Chicago.

PLANTS:

Hammond maintains four plants in the Chicago area.
Hammond products are distributed by over 750 retail
outlets throughout the U.S.

Wells Lamont Corp., a wholly-owned subsidiary,
maintains nine plants in Arkansas, Louisiana, Mississippi, New York, Oklahoma and Tennessee. Its line of
work and sports gloves are sold in over 150,000 retail

(Hammond Corporation, continued)
outlets, including Sears, Roebuck and many hardware
stores and golf pro shops.

The Everett Piano Co. is located in South Haven,
Michigan.

Gibbs Mfg. & Research is located in Janesville, Wisconsin.

HARVARD INDUSTRIES
P.O. Box 527
Farmingdale, New Jersey 07727
(201) 938–9221

MAJOR PRODUCTS:

Aluminum products, office furniture, aerospace and electronic components, rocket launchers, ceramic tile, molded fiberglass, kitchen and bathroom products, air freight and passenger service, service station equipment, printing

CONSUMER BRANDS:

Selectile ceramic tile

FINANCIAL DATA:

	$ Millions	1969	1968
Net Sales		113.1	113.7
Net Income		1.6	3.9

ANTI-PERSONNEL CONTRACTS:

[Contracts were held by Alsco, now a division of Harvard Industries]

2/67—$156,938 for XM157/A launchers for 2.75 inch rockets

12/67—$271,733 for XM157/B launchers for 2.75 inch rockets

6/68—$328,835 for XM157/B launchers for 2.75 inch rockets

(Harvard Industries, continued)

$2.6 million for XM159/C launchers for 2.75 inch rockets

OFFICERS AND DIRECTORS:

President: William D. Hurley (Chairman/President: Alsco, Inc.)

OUTSIDE DIRECTORS:

George W. Anderson
Detler W. Bronk
Walter M. Jeffords
Caleb B. Laning
Morris N. Natelson: Partner, Lehman Brothers

ANNUAL MEETING:

The annual meeting is held in December.

PLANT SITES AND SERVICES:

Harvard Industries maintains plants in Farmingdale and Shrewsbury, New Jersey; Quakertown, Lewisburg, and Philadelphia, Pennsylvania; Oakland, Poco Rivera, and Glendale, California; Miami, Florida; Enid, Oklahoma; and Wichita Falls, Texas.

Franklin Press, a wholly-owned subsidiary, is in Miami, Florida.

Transarctic, Inc., formed by Harvard Ind. in 1969, operates air freight and passenger service to Alaska's North Slope oil fields.

Alsco, Inc. produced anti-personnel weapons at the Techfab Division plant in St. Louis, Missouri.

HAYES-ALBION
437 Fern Avenue
Jackson, Michigan
(517) 782–9421

MAJOR PRODUCTS:

Automotive supplies, textiles, die castings, rockets and components

CONSUMER BRANDS:

Palm-N-Turn containers, *Airmaster* fans

FINANCIAL DATA:

$ Millions	7/31/69*	1968	1967
Net Sales	100.2	89.2	83.8
Net Income	6.4	6.9	6.8
P/E Ratio	15–7	14–10	12–7
Yr End Mkt Value	51.5		

ANTI-PERSONNEL CONTRACTS:

6 to 12/68—$3.1 million for M151 warheads and 2.75 inch launchers and rockets

1/69—$2.1 million for metal parts for 2.75 inch rockets

4/69—$2.0 million for metal parts for 2.75 inch rocket warheads

FY 69—$1.3 million for 2.75 inch rocket warheads

---

* Hayes-Albion's annual accounting period ends on July 31 of each calendar year.

122

(Hayes-Albion, continued)
OFFICERS AND DIRECTORS:

Chairman: C. L. Carter (Director: City Bank and Trust Co.)
President: C. E. Drury

OUTSIDE DIRECTORS:

F. A. Bond: Professor/Dean, Graduate School of Business Administration, University of Michigan
G. M. Brown: President, Automatic Steel Products
J. H. Campbell: President, Consumer's Power Co.
A. B. Connable: President, LaFourche Realty Co.
P. M. Detwiler: Vice-President, E. F. Hutton & Co.
E. C. Hetherwick: Chairman, Plastigage Corp.
C. Hollerith: Vice-President, Walstrom Products, Inc.
D. T. McCone: President, Aeroquip Corp.
C. F. Spaeth: Former Chairman, Honorary Chairman, City Bank & Trust Co., Jackson, Michigan

ANNUAL MEETING:

The annual meeting of shareholders is customarily held during November at the corporate offices in Jackson, Michigan.

PLANTS:

Hayes-Albion maintains plants in Albion, Bay City, Hillsdale, Jackson, Milan, Parma and Whitmore Lake, Mich.; Bryan, Spencerville, Tiffin and West Unity, Ohio; Charlotte and Winston-Salem, N.C.; and Simpsonville, S.C.

(Hayes-Albion, continued)

Mortar shell and rocket bodies for the military are cast at Albion and machined at Hillsdale.

CORPORATE PHILOSOPHY:

The May 11, 1970 issue of *Aerospace Daily* reported that Hayes-Albion was completing all of its defense work by June 30, 1970.

HERCULES, INC.
910 Market Street
Wilmington, Delaware 19898
(302) 658–9811

MAJOR PRODUCTS:

Protein products, explosives, polymers, fibers, modular housing

CONSUMER BRANDS:

Red Dot rifle powder, *Herban* herbicide, *Hercules Wear Tape*, *Nitroform* fertilizer, *Woodweld* adhesive, *Haskon* plastic bottles

FINANCIAL DATA:

$ Millions	1969	1968	1967
Net Sales	746.0	718.3	642.6
Net Income	43.9	53.3	46.7
P/E Ratio	24–14	21–12	23–18
Yr End Mkt Value	612.9		

ANTI-PERSONNEL CONTRACTS:

$9.4 million to load, assemble and pack XM41E1 mines into CNU–4/3 canisters

9/67–$222,136 for development and study of XM45E1 gravel mines

1/68–$48,662 for development and study of XM45E1 gravel mines

(Hercules, Inc., continued)

OFFICERS AND DIRECTORS:

Chairman: Elmer Hinner, Mendenhall, Pennsylvania
  (Chairman: Hystron Fibers, Inc.)
Chairman: Henry Thouron, Wilmington, Delaware
  (Trustee: Wesley College; Director: National In-
  dustrial Conference Board)
President: Werner C. Brown, Greenville, Delaware

OUTSIDE DIRECTORS:

Joseph A. Thomas: Senior Partner, Lehman Bros.
William Kendall: President, Louisville & Nashville
  Railroad Co.

ANNUAL MEETING:

The annual meeting is customarily held during
March at the Hercules Research Center in New
Castle County, Delaware.

PLANTS:

Bacchus, Utah; Bessemer, Ala.; Brunswick, Oxford
and Savannah, Ga.; Burlington, Gibbstown and
Parlin, N.J.; Carthage and Louisiana, Mo.; Chicopee,
Mass.; Covington, Franklin, Hopewell, Va.; Donora
and Washington, Pa.; Eugene and Portland, Ore.;
Gilbert, Minn.; Glens Falls, Port Ewen, N.Y.; Harbor
Beach, Ishpeming, Kalamazoo, Mich.; Hattiesburg,
Miss.; Hercules, Richmond, Cal.; Houston, Texas;
Jacksonville, Ark.; Kenvil, N.J.; Lake Charles, Pla-
quemine, La.; Milwaukee, Wisc.; Pulaski, Va.; Re-
search Triangle Park, Wilmington, N.C.; Rocket

(Hercules, Inc., continued)
Center, W. Va.; Spartanburg, S.C.; Tacoma, Wash.;
Terre Haute, Ind.; Hercules Research Center, Wilmington, Del.
Government-owned plants operated by Hercules are:
Radford Army Ammunition Plant, Radford, Va.;
Sunflower Army Ammunition Plant, Lawrence,
Kansas.

On March 2, 1970, Hercules announced acquisition
of Black Crow and Eidsness, Inc., a Gainesville, Fla.
environmental engineering concern.

HOFFMAN ELECTRONICS CORPORATION
Hoffman Electronic Park
El Monte, California 91734
(213) 442–0123

MAJOR PRODUCTS:

Diodes, solar cells, special electronic equipment for the government

CONSUMER BRANDS:

Mark IV audio/visual system

FINANCIAL DATA:

$ Millions	1969	1968	1967
Net Sales	30.5	23.8	22.0
Net Income	.6	.6	−1.08
Yr End Mkt Value	17.3		

ANTI-PERSONNEL CONTRACTS:

FY 68–$9.1 million for fin and nozzle assemblies for 2.75 inch rockets

OFFICERS AND DIRECTORS:

Chairman: H. Leslie Hoffman, San Marino, California (Director: Norris Industries, Pacific Lighting Corp., AMFAC, Inc.)
President: David C. Arnold

(Hoffman Electronics Corporation, continued)

OUTSIDE DIRECTORS:

Earl C. Adams: Vice-President/Comptroller, Dania
  Bank, Dania, Florida
Robert R. Dockson
A. R. Hoeffer
Richard Lyon
H. Safford Nye—Management Consultant, Director,
  Norris Industries

ANNUAL MEETING:

The annual meeting is held during May in El
Monte, California.

PLANTS:

Hoffman Electronics maintains a plant in El
Monte, California. Corporate research facilities are
located in Santa Barbara, California.
Lance Antenna, a wholly owned subsidiary, operates
two plants in southern Indiana.

HONEYWELL, INC.
2701 4th Avenue
Minneapolis, Minnesota 55408
(612) 332–5200

MAJOR PRODUCTS:

Automatic control devices and systems; thermostatic devices

CONSUMER BRANDS:

Pentax, Rollei, and *Stronobar* cameras and photographic equipment; *Minneapolis-Honeywell* control devices; *Takumar* lenses; *Elmo* cameras and projectors

FINANCIAL DATA:

$ Millions	1969	1968	1967
Net Sales	1426.0	1281.3	1044.9
Net Income	62.5	50.5	42.3
P/E Ratio	38–26	41–26	41–22
Yr End Mkt Value	2120.1		

ANTI-PERSONNEL CONTRACTS:

Honeywell is by far the largest producer of anti-personnel weapons and components, with contracts totalling over $250 million. They produce both entire weapons systems and components.

6/66—$65.2 million for BLU–42/B and BLU–52/B mines and SUU–38/A Tactical Fighter Dispenser Munitions

(Honeywell, Inc., continued)

7/67–$7.0 million increment for XM54 white phosphorus anti-personnel mines

10/67–$16.5 million installment on total contract of $33 million for XM54 white phosphorus anti-personnel mines

12/67–$1.0 million for SUU–13/A dispenser and adapter cables

Rockeye II cluster bombs—(accelerated development on this weapon in FY 1967 for Vietnam) Honeywell produces the dispensers, tail sections, empty bomblets, and the XM224 bomblet fuse; Crane Arsenal loads the bomblets and packages the Rockeye dispenser

1/68–$24.9 million initial award on a $49.8 million contract for BLU–42A/B and BLU–54/B mines and SUU–38/A Tactical Fighter Dispenser Munitions

5/68–$91,080 Research and Development for study of aerial mining system

9/68–$2.8 million fixed-price contract for metal parts for BLU–26/B "guava" bombs

10/68–$3.4 million modification on Rockeye II cluster bombs

11/68–$12.2 million increment to a $24.4 million fixed-price contract for BLU–26/B "guava" bombs

1/69–$1.3 million contract modification for bomblet fuses

1/69–$3.1 million for BLU–26/B "guava" bomb

(Honeywell, Inc., continued)

components; $4.5 million for carbon steel balls and metal parts for BLU–26/B "guava" bombs, BLU–36/B "guava" bombs, and BLU–59/B bombs

5/69—$9.3 million Navy contract modification on Rockeye II cluster bombs

6/69—$1.2 million contract modification for bomblet fuses

9/69—$3.6 million for CBU–55/B (Honeywell is the sole source of dispenser, bomblets, and bomblet fuse) from the Navy—which has requested $9.6 million for this weapon for FY 1970

10/69—$14.2 million for Rockeye II components

10/69—$1.6 million for "component parts for anti-personnel munitions"

FY 69—Research and Development on the Special Purposes Individual Weapon (SPIW) for firing Beehive and flechette projectiles

3/70—$12.1 million for Rockeye II components

OFFICERS AND DIRECTORS:

Chairman: James Binger, Wayzata, Minnesota (Director: Northwest Airlines, Northwestern Bell Telephone, Northwest Bancorporation)

President: Stephen Keating, Wayzata, Minnesota (Director: First Bank System, General Mills, Toro Manufacturing Company, Dayton Corporation)

OUTSIDE DIRECTORS:

Bruce Dayton: President and Director, Dayton Cor-

(Honeywell, Inc., continued)
poration

Neil McKinnon: Chairman, Canadian Imperial Bank of Commerce

Leo Schoenhofen: President and Director, Marcor, Inc.

Donald Nyrop: President and Director, Northwest Airlines

Paul Gerot: Former President, Pillsbury Company

John J. Wilson: Secretary, Massachusetts Institute of Technology

Paul Wishart: Former President, Honeywell

W. W. Finke: President and Director, Dictaphone Corporation

E. J. McNeely: Retired President, AT&T

ANNUAL MEETING:

The annual meeting is held during April in Minneapolis, Minnesota.

PLANTS AND FACILITIES:

Systems and Research Division of the Aerospace and Defense Group maintains labs in Minneapolis and Boston, Mass.

Ordnance Division plants are in Minneapolis; Seattle, Wash.; Los Angeles, Cal.; Montgomeryville, Pa. Other Honeywell labs and plants are located in Freeport, Warren, and Chicago, Ill.; Wabash, Ind.; Akron, Ohio; Peterborough and Manchester, N.H.; Philadelphia, Pa.; Denver, Colo.; Annapolis, Md.;

(Honeywell, Inc., continued)
St. Petersburg, Fla.; Brighton, Waltham, Lawrence, Lowell, and Framingham, Mass.; Ft. Washington, Pa.; Hopkins and New Brighton, Minn.; W. Covina, Gardena, and San Diego, Cal.

CORPORATE PHILOSOPHY:

In response to pressure from the Honeywell Project to discontinue their production of anti-personnel weapons, Honeywell released this statement to the press in April, 1969:

> Honeywell management shares the feeling of those who would like to see the Vietnam War ended. We vigorously support the efforts the government is making to find a solution to the complex problems that surround this conflict. Until such solutions are found we believe the government has an obligation to provide our armed forces engaged in the conflict with the equipment they need to maintain a strong military posture. As a technologically-based company we have the ability to provide a variety of equipment as a supplier to the defense department. We believe it is entirely appropriate and correct to do so as a matter of good citizenship. For those who do not share our views about chosen government we endorse their right to legal and peaceful protest.

Honeywell has advertised in *Ordnance* magazine: "We stand ready to build weapons that work, to build them fast and to build them in quantity."

HOUSEHOLD FINANCE COMPANY
Suite 3201, Prudential Plaza
Chicago, Illinois 60601
(312) 944-7174

MAJOR PRODUCTS:

Lending operations, home furnishings, cold storage
devices, retailing

CONSUMER BRANDS:

Thermos consumer products, *Structo* toys, charcoal
grills, *Halsey-Taylor* drinking fountains, *Scotsman*
products, *National, E-Z Haul* rentals, *Chef-o-matic,
Almco, Ropaco, Dinex*

FINANCIAL DATA:

	$ Millions	1969	1968
Net Sales		1,543.4	1,408.7
Net Income		82.6	79.8
P/E Ratio			17–10
Yr End Mkt Value		852.3	

ANTI-PERSONNEL CONTRACTS:

[Contracts are held by King-Seeley Thermos Co., a
   subsidiary of Household Finance Co.]
9/68—$77,220 for M1A4 fin assemblies for fragmen-
   tation bombs
12/68—$70,142 for M1A4 fin assemblies for fragmen-
   tation bombs

(Household Finance Company, continued)

OFFICERS AND DIRECTORS:

Chairman: H. E. MacDonald, Glencoe, Illinois

President: Arthur E. Rasmussen, Jr., Upper Montclair, N.J.

OUTSIDE DIRECTORS:

Richard de LaChappelle: Partner, Dean Witter and Company

R. H. Matson: Corporate Consultant

G. M. Mott: President, Coldwell, Banker and Company

G. W. Rauch: Member, Hubachek, Kelly, Miller, Rauch, and Kirby

A. O. Steffy: President, City Products Corporation

Miller Upton: President, Beloit College

ANNUAL MEETING:

The annual meeting is customarily held during April at the Prudential Plaza in Chicago.

PLANTS, SERVICES AND STORES:

HFC owns the Ben Franklin chain of stores with over 2,200 franchised units nationwide.

HFC owns the T. G. & Y. and Scott variety stores chain, with over 750 stores in the South and the Midwest.

Other merchandisers owned by HFC are: Von's su-

(Household Finance Company, continued)
permarkets, headquartered in Los Angeles, with 87
stores in Southern California;

Coast-to-Coast stores, with over 1000 stores in the
West and the Midwest;

White stores, with over 500 stores in the South and
Southwest;

A total of 68 home furnishing and furniture stores:
Barker Brothers of Southern California;

Gold's Furniture and Appliances, of southern California;

Dryer's Furniture, of San Diego, California;

American Furniture, of San Antonio, Texas;

Miller Desk, a nationwide chain;

Huffman-Koos, of New Jersey;

Colby Home Furnishings, of metropolitan Chicago;

Butler Brothers' Department Stores, of metropolitan
Los Angeles and Seattle.

Household Finance Company, Inc. is the largest consumer loan service with over 1500 branch offices.

HFC owns the National Car Rental System, which
has over 1800 rental outlets.

HFC acquired the King-Seeley Thermos Co. in
August, 1968. King-Seeley maintains plants in Al-
bert Lea, Minnesota; Ann Arbor, Michigan; Freeport,
and Macomb, Illinois and Norwich, Connecticut.
King-Seeley recently acquired the Halsey W. Taylor
Co. of Warren, Ohio.

KDI CORPORATION
5721 Dragon Way
Cincinnati, Ohio 45227
(513) 272–1421

MAJOR PRODUCTS:

Machinery, tools, high speed printers, software, school furniture, films, textbooks

FINANCIAL DATA:

$ Millions	1969	1968	1967
Net Sales	125.0	30.5	14.0
Net Income	4.0	2.7	1.1

ANTI-PERSONNEL CONTRACTS:

6 to 12/68—$1.5 million for M427 impact mechanical point detonating (P.D.) fuse for 2.75 inch rockets

6 to 12 /68—$1.5 million for safety and arming devices for M429 proximity fuse for 2.75 inch rockets

2/69—$2.6 million for metal parts for 2.75 inch rocket fuses

4/69—$1.4 million contract modification for M427 P.D. fuses

5/69—$1.1 million contract modification for safety and arming devices for M429 fuses

6/69—$1.3 million contract modification for metal parts for 2.75 inch rocket fuses

12/69—$1.5 million—metal parts for 2.75 inch rocket fuses

(KDI Corporation, continued)
OFFICERS AND DIRECTORS:

Chairman: C. B. Akers
President: Walter G. Cox, Cincinnati, Ohio (Chairman: Aerospace Research Corp., Inland Communications)

OUTSIDE DIRECTORS:

Donald Chadwick
Norman Collister
Rolf H. Brookes
F. L. Bryant
J. G. Lippincott

PLANT SITES:

The main plant of KDI Corp. is in Cincinnati, Ohio.
KDI owns Aqua Systems, Inc. of California.
Neptune Engineering Corp., a KDI subsidiary, is located in Norfolk, Virginia.
S.C.O.R.E., a KDI subsidiary, manufactures thermal batteries at its plant in Cockeysville, Maryland.
Holex Corp., a San Francisco-based subsidiary of KDI, produces electro-explosive devices.
Empire Products, a subsidiary of KDI, is located in Cincinnati. Ohio.

KISSELL COMPANY
30 Warder Street
Springfield, Ohio 45501
(513) 325–7651

MAJOR PRODUCTS:

Mortgage banking

FINANCIAL DATA:

$ Millions	1968	1967	1966
Net Sales	6.4	5.8	4.7
Net Income	.7	.6	.1

ANTI-PERSONNEL CONTRACTS:

[Contracts are held by Kisco Corp., a Kissell subsidiary]

FY 69—$13.4 million for M1484 cartridge cases for 105mm flechette and smoke projectiles

OFFICERS AND DIRECTORS:

Chairman: Howard B. Noonan
President: Philip L. Greenawalt, Springfield, Ohio

OUTSIDE DIRECTORS:

Ralph R. Baldenhofer: President, Thompson Grinder Co.

Louis Dolan: Executive Vice-President, Gamble-Skogmo, Inc.

William B. F. Hall: Chairman, Colonial Mortgage Co.

(Kissell Company, continued)
John F. Havens
Paul F. Hellmuth: Managing Partner, Hale & Dore
   Co.
Peter K. Noonan

ANNUAL MEETING:

The annual meeting is held during April at the corporate headquarters in Springfield, Ohio.

PLANTS AND SERVICES:

Kissell Company maintains branches in Akron, Cincinnati, Cleveland, Columbus, Dayton, Lima, Springfield and Toledo, Ohio; Anaheim, San Diego, San Francisco and Tarzana, California; Lexington and Louisville, Kentucky; Atlanta, Georgia; Charleston, West Virginia; Detroit, Michigan; Indianapolis, Indiana; Pittsburgh, Pennsylvania.

Kisco Corp., the contract-holding subsidiary of Kissell, produces anti-personnel weapons at its plant in St. Louis, Missouri.

MARTIN-MARIETTA CORPORATION
277 Park Avenue
New York, New York 10017
(212) 826–5050

MAJOR PRODUCTS:

Aerospace products (Titan, Sprint missiles), cement, insulators, inks, dyes

FINANCIAL DATA:

$ Millions	1969	1968	1967
Net Sales	981.4	682.0	695.6
Net Income	44.2	40.2	36.6
P/E Ratio		15–9	16–12
Yr End Mkt Value	457.2		

ANTI-PERSONNEL CONTRACTS:

$900,000 for development of anti-personnel version of Bullpup B air-surface missile

$2.4 million for canisters for aerial mine system

OFFICERS AND DIRECTORS:

President: George M. Bunker, Washington, D.C. (Director: Bulova Watch Co., Nuclear Corp. of America, Fla. Capital Corp., American Security & Trust Co., Bunker-Ramo Corp., Washington Senators)

OUTSIDE DIRECTORS:

William A. Burns: Former President, Trailmobile

(Martin-Marietta Corporation, continued)

Corp.; Lecturer, University of California (Berkeley)

Leigh R. Gignilliat, Jr.: Associate, Rodman-Renshaw

John E. Parker: Former Chairman, Chairman Exec. Comm./Director, Bunker-Ramo Corp.

John L. Sullivan: Senior Partner, Sullivan, Shea & Kenney

Robert M. McKinney: Editor/Publisher, Santa Fe *New Mexican,* Espanola *New Mexican,* Los Alamos *New Mexican,* Taos *News,* Las Vegas *Optic,* Monte Vista *Journal*

William W. Hagerty: President, Drexel Institute of Technology

Curtis E. Jones: Vice-President, Mellon National Bank & Trust Co.

William I. Spencer: Executive Vice-President, First National City Bank

Eugene Zuckert: Counsel, Lear, Scoutt & Rasenberger; Former Assistant Secretary of the Air Force

ANNUAL MEETING:

The annual meeting is customarily held during January at the Barbizon-Plaza Hotel in New York City.

PLANTS:

Aerospace and defense plants are located in Orlando, Florida and Denver Colorado.

(Martin-Marietta Corporation, continued)
Other plants are in: New York, Indiana, Georgia, Maryland, Kentucky, North Carolina, Arkansas, Florida, Illinois, Iowa, Pennsylvania, Ohio, California, Texas, Virginia, Colorado, Minnesota, Michigan, Missouri, Wisconsin, Massachusetts, West Virginia, Alabama, Kansas, Louisiana, Tennessee, Connecticut, Arizona, Oklahoma, Maine, Washington, New Jersey and Oregon.

Martin-Marietta owns 82.7% of the stock of Harvey Aluminum which owns plants at The Dalles, Oregon; Torrance, California; Adrian, Michigan; and Lewisport, Kentucky. They also operate an Army ordnance plant at Milan, Tennessee.

Other Martin-Marietta subsidiaries are: Aetna Portland Cement, Capitol Cement, Concrete Products Services, Dewey Portland Cement, Dewey Rocky Mountain Cement, Dragon Cement, Southern Cement, Standard Lime and Refractories, Madison Silos, Manley Sand, Master Builders, Sinclair and Valentine, Southern Dyestuff, Appalachian Stone, Concrete, Materials and Superior Stone.

On April 3, 1970, Martin-Marietta announced that it was acquiring the assets of Weston and Brooker Company of Columbia, South Carolina. The company, which operates four quarries, will be operated as a unit of Superior Stone.

MOTOROLA, INC.
9401 West Grand Avenue
Franklin Park, Illinois 60131
(312) 451–1000

MAJOR PRODUCTS:

Communications equipment, electronics for military and automotive products

CONSUMER BRANDS:

Motorola television, radios, phonographs and components

FINANCIAL DATA:

	$ Millions	1969	1968	1967
Net Sales		873.2	775.1	630.0
Net Income		33.8	28.2	18.8
P/E Ratio			33–21	47–29
Yr End Mkt Value		896.0		

ANTI-PERSONNEL CONTRACTS:

$242,880 for integrated circuits for XM429 2.75 inch rocket fuses

OFFICERS AND DIRECTORS:

Chairman: Robert W. Galvin, Barrington, Illinois (Trustee: Illinois Institute of Technology; Lay Trustee: Notre Dame University; Director: Harris Trust & Savings Bank)

(Motorola, Inc., continued)
President: Elmer H. Wavering, Glenview, Illinois

OUTSIDE DIRECTORS:

Arthur C. Nielson: President/Director, A. C. Nielson Co.
Elmer H. Schulz: Executive Vice-President/Director, ITT Research Institute
Kenneth V. Zweener: Chairman, Harris Trust & Savings Bank

ANNUAL MEETING:

The annual meeting of shareholders is held during May in Franklin Park, Illinois.

PLANTS:
Research and Development center for military division is in Scottsdale, Arizona.

Other plants are in: Chicago, Franklin Park, Elgin, Pontiac, Schaumberg, Elk Grove and Quincy, Ill.; Arcade, N.Y.; Phoenix and Mesa, Ariz.

On April 6, 1970, Motorola announced that it had permanently closed its only color-television-tube facility, the Franklin Park, Illinois plant, and sold machinery and equipment to General Telephone and Electronics.

NATIONAL LEAD COMPANY
111 Broadway
New York, New York 10006
(212) 732–9400

MAJOR PRODUCTS:

Number one producer of lead products, paint, bearings, oil drilling, chemicals and plastics

CONSUMER BRANDS:

Dutch Boy paint

FINANCIAL DATA:

$ Millions	1969	1968	1967
Net Sales	929.8	858.2	818.9
Net Income	50.7	49.9	51.3
P/E Ratio	18–11	19–14	16–13
Yr End Mkt Value	599.2		

ANTI-PERSONNEL CONTRACTS:

FY 68—$3.1 million for BLU–26/B "guava" bomblet metal parts

9/68—$1.4 million for BLU–26/B "guava" metal parts

1/69—$1.9 million for BLU–26/B "guava" bomb components

11/69—$2.7 million for metal parts for bombs

(National Lead Company, continued)

OFFICERS AND DIRECTORS:

Chairman: Edward R. Rowley, Saddle River, New Jersey

President: J. B. Henrich, Darien, Connecticut (Director: Baker Castor Oil Co., Morris P. Kirk & Son)

OUTSIDE DIRECTORS:

E. J. Hanley: Chairman, Allegheny Ludlum Steel Corp.

R. M. Paget: Partner, Cresap, McCormack & Paget

W. J. Welch: Vice President, Southern Screw Co.

M. H. Wright: General Partner, Kuhn, Loeb & Co.

ANNUAL MEETING:

The annual meeting is held during April in Newark, New Jersey.

PLANTS:

Divisions of National Lead are located in Indianapolis, Ind.; Charleston, W.Va.; Granite City and Chicago, Ill.; Landover, Md.; Albany, New York City, Batavia and Depew, N.Y.; Statesville, N.C.; Perth Amboy and Bayonne, N.J.; Cincinnati, Cleveland, Toledo and Fernald, Ohio; Dallas, Houston, Laredo and Sweetwater, Texas; Oakland, Los Angeles, San Francisco and Southgate, Cal.; Philadelphia and Pittsburgh, Pa.; Malvern, Ark.; Memphis and Rockwood, Tenn.; Detroit, Grand Rapids, Mich.; South-

(National Lead Company, continued)
shore, Ky.; St. Louis Park, Minn.; Salt Lake City,
Utah; Granite City, Pottstown and St. Louis, Mo.; and
Henderson, Nevada.

National Lead owns the Lake View Trust and Savings Bank in Chicago.

NATIONAL UNION ELECTRIC COMPANY
Cummings Point
Stamford, Connecticut
(203) 325-2601

MAJOR PRODUCTS:

Home entertainment products, wood cabinets, vacuum cleaners, air conditioners, missile components

CONSUMER BRANDS:

Modul-Air, Kompact, Quiet Kool air conditioners, *Emerson, DuMont, Pilot* home entertainment producducts (TV's, radios, record players), *Eureka* vacuum cleaners

FINANCIAL DATA:

	$ Millions	1969	1968	1967
Net Sales		151.4	149.8	134.4
Net Income		3.2	4.2	3.4
P/E Ratio			19–8	19–10
Yr End Mkt Value		27.5		

ANTI-PERSONNEL CONTRACTS:

11/67—$3.3 million for fuse parts for bomblet dispensers

OFFICERS AND DIRECTORS:

Chairman and President: C. Russell Feldman

(National Union Electric Company, continued)

OUTSIDE DIRECTORS:

Arthur H. Dean: Partner, Sullivan & Cromwell
Harry C. Mills

ANNUAL MEETING:

The annual meeting is customarily held during May
in Wilmington, Delaware.

PLANTS:

National Union Electric owns plants in Bloomington,
Illinois; Jersey City, New Jersey; Napoleon, Ohio
and Canosotota, New York.

CORPORATE PHILOSOPHY:

National Union Electric owns 17% of the stock of
National Presto Industries, producers of "Presto"
electrical appliances and military ordnance (105mm
and 8″ shells). On December 15, 1969, National Union
reported that they were abandoning their plans to
attempt to purchase the remaining stock due to
"present market conditions." The main offices of National Presto are in Eau Claire, Wisconsin.

NORRIS INDUSTRIES, INC.
5215 South Boyle Avenue
Los Angeles, California 90058
(213) 588–7111

MAJOR PRODUCTS:

Metal products for construction and other industries, electric and gas ranges, door locks (Weiser Division is number one supplier of residential locks in North America), military products (63% of sales), bombs, mortar shells, and missile system components, auto pollution abatement kits, natural gas conversion kits.

CONSUMER BRANDS:

Fyr-Fyter fire extinguishers, *Thermador* ovens, *Wasteking* home appliances, *Weiser* locks, *Pyrene* fire extinguishers

FINANCIAL DATA:

$ Millions	7/31/69*	1968	1967
Net Sales	281.8	274.0	190.0
Net Income	14.4	14.4	10.7
P/E Ratio	9–5	10–6	10–4
Yr End Mkt Value	75.5		

ANTI-PERSONNEL CONTRACTS:

6 to 12/68—$11.0 million for tubes for 2.75 inch rockets

* Norris Industries' annual accounting period ends on July 31 of each calendar year.

(Norris Industries, Inc., continued)
11/69—$3.9 million for 2.75 inch rocket motor tubes
$1.0 million for cartridge cases for M377 90mm
flechettes

OFFICERS AND DIRECTORS:

Chairman: Kenneth T. Norris, San Marino, California (Director: L.A. World Affairs Council; Trustee: Occidental College, University of Southern
California)

President: Kenneth T. Norris, Jr., San Marino, California (Director: Fyr-Fyter)

OUTSIDE DIRECTORS:

J. S. Griffith: Owner, John S. Griffith Properties

H. L. Hoffman: Chairman, Hoffman Electronics

Willard W. Keith: Director/Member Exec. Committee, Marsh & McLennan, Inc.

H. S. Hazeltine: Partner, Adams, Dugue & Hazeltine; Secretary, Hoffman Electronics

H. Safford Nye: Management Consultant; Director,
Hoffman Electronics

M. E. Arnold: President, Music Center Operating
Co.

ANNUAL MEETING:

The annual meeting is held during November in Los
Angeles.

PLANTS:

Norris maintains plants in Los Angeles, Poco Rivera

(Norris Industries, Inc., continued)

and Riverbank, Cal., Everett and Brockton, Mass.; Newark and E. Brunswick, N.J. and City of Industry and South Gate, Cal.

Waste King Corp., a Norris subsidiary, is in Los Angeles.

CORPORATE POSTURE:

In an ad in the *Wall Street Journal* of June 2, 1968, Norris stated that " . . . from a solid base of military and commercial business, we've expanded further into industrial and construction markets. When the abnormal military requirements taper off (which we certainly hope will be soon), we're ready to grow in other directions."

In *Forbes,* April 1, 1968: "In percentage terms, Norris, Industries, may well be the biggest corporate beneficiary of the Vietnam War. Between 1965 and its fiscal year ending July 31, Norris Industries' sales will have mushroomed from $67 million to about $250 million. . . . By that time, some $150 million of Norris' sales, or around ⅔ of the total, will be derived from Vietnam.

"With that background (after WW II and Korea—business dropped way down from $26 million during WW II to $6.5 million after V-J Day and $65 million as a result of Korea to $37 million after Korea), it is surprising that Norris elected the wartime route a third time. 'Why shouldn't we?' Norris

(Norris Industries, Inc., continued)
shoots back when asked the question. 'Look, we're the best in the business, over the years we've improved our technical know-how.'

"A better explanation would seem to be that the family-dominated Norris Industries simply had nothing better in the offing. Its pre-Vietnam business consisted of an uninspiring collection of built-in kitchen appliances, plumbingware, industrial fasteners, gas cylinders, automobile wheels and electrical outlet boxes. . . . Riding the war-contract roller coaster was simply the best prospect Norris had.

"Norris has therefore been using its time of prosperity to line up some other things to cushion the blow. One is recently-acquired Waste King Corp., a maker of garbage disposals, dishwashers and built-in kitchen equipment. . . . It, plus a substantial portion of Norris' other businesses (locks, plumbing fixtures, electrical outlet boxes), is closely tied to the residential construction market. . . .

"The younger Norris says: 'Being in the residential housing field is a balance for us. When the war ends, credit will become easier to obtain and home construction will climb.' Even should this hope come true, the fact remains that Norris' over-all sales and profits will come tumbling down when the Vietnam war ends and a far bigger and healthier acquisition than Waste King could do little to lessen the sting of losing $95–115 million in sales. Norris may have

(Norris Industries, Inc., continued)
learned how to enjoy momentary success and still roll away from a knockout punch. But at the end of the fight, it seems certain to come out bruised once again."

NORTHROP CORPORATION
9744 Wilshire Boulevard
Beverly Hills, California 90212
(213) 675–4611

MAJOR PRODUCTS:

Aircraft and parts, spacecraft systems, navigation systems, chemicals, aluminum products, communication systems

CONSUMER BRANDS:

Hallicrafters radios and components

FINANCIAL DATA:

$ Millions	7/31/69*	1968	1967
Net Sales	561.2	485.5	469.4
Net Income	18.5	15.7	12.6
P/E Ratio	14–9	17–9	16–9
Yr End Mkt Value	168.9		

ANTI-PERSONNEL CONTRACTS:

$429,600 for design, development and testing of a flechette area neutralization gun

6 to 12/68—$3.4 million for WDU–4A/A flechette warhead for 2.75 inch rockets

$3.7 million for 105mm Beehive projectiles

5/69—$4.2 million for WDU–4A/A

1/70—$1.5 million for flechette warheads

* Northrop's annual accounting period ends on July 31 of each calendar year.

(Northrop Corporation, continued)

OFFICERS AND DIRECTORS:

Chairman and President: Thomas V. Jones, Los Angeles, Cal. (Trustee: Stanford University; Director: Times-Mirror Co.; Member: Department of Defense Industry Advisory Council; Director: L. A. World Affairs Council)

OUTSIDE DIRECTORS:

Earle M. Jorgenson: Chairman, Earl M. Jorgenson Co.

T. M. McDaniel, Jr.: President/Director, Southern California Edison Co.

Richard Millar: Vice-Chairman, Glore Forgan, William R. Staats Co.

John O'Melveny: Senior Partner, O'Melveny & Myers

C. L. Peck, Jr.: President, C. L. Peck Contractor

A. E. Ponting: Chairman Exec. Comm., Director, Blyth & Co.

Richard P. Codey: President, Wells Fargo Co.

ANNUAL MEETING:

The annual meeting is customarily held in Hawthorne, California, during December.

PLANTS AND OFFICES:

Principal plant sites are in Hawthorne, Palos Verdes, Peninsula, Anaheim and Newbury Park, California. Hallicrafters (100% owned by Northrop) is located in Rolling Meadows, Illinois.

(Northrop Corporation, continued)

Regional and district offices are in: Washington, D.C.;
Dayton, Ohio; Lexington, Mass.; Oklahoma City,
Okla.; Honolulu, Hawaii; Ft. Walton Beach, Fla.;
Eatontown, N.J.; Rome, N.Y.; San Antonio, Texas,
and San Bernadino, Cal.

REYNOLDS METALS COMPANY
6601 Broad Street
Richmond, Virginia 23230
(703) 282–2311

MAJOR PRODUCTS:

Primary aluminum and industrial aluminum products, plastic film products, aluminum packaging products, cans, aluminum siding, doors, windows

CONSUMER BRAND:

Reynolds

FINANCIAL DATA:

$ Millions	1969	1968	1967
Net Sales	1012.7	843.8	804.0
Net Income	55.1	29.6	52.3
P/E Ratio	15–9	33–21	23–17
Yr End Mkt Value	492.4		

ANTI-PERSONNEL CONTRACTS:

$1.05 million for 2.75 inch rocket components

OFFICERS AND DIRECTORS:

Chairman: Richard S. Reynolds, Jr., Richmond, Virginia (Chairman: Robertshaw Controls Co.; Director: Central National Bank, British Aluminum Co., Manufacturers Hanover Trust Co., Lawyer's Title Insurance Corp., Richmond Corp.)

(Reynolds Metals Company, continued)

President: Joseph H. McConnell, Midlothian, Virginia (Director: Basic, Inc.; First and Merchants National Bank; British Aluminum Co.)

OUTSIDE DIRECTORS:

C. F. Manning: Ret. Vice-President, Reynolds Metals Co.

John H. Krey: Chairman Finance Committee/Director, Robertshaw Controls Co.

W. T. Brunot: Finance Director, British Aluminum

Thomas Arden: President, Robertshaw Controls Co.

ANNUAL MEETING:

The annual meeting is customarily held during April in the Reynolds Metals Bldg., Richmond, Virginia.

PLANTS:

Plants are located in Corpus Christi and Houston, Texas; Hurricane Creek, Arkadelphia, Jones Mills and Malvern, Ark.; Listerhill, Sheffield and Birmingham, Ala.; Longview, Wash.; Massena, N.Y.; Troutdale, Ore.; Louisville, Ky.; Richmond, Bellwood and Grottoes, Va.; McCook, Ill.; Atlanta, Ga.; Grand Rapids, Mich.; Phoenix, Ariz.; Torrance, Cal.; Chester, Pa.; St. Louis, Mo.; Tampa, Fla; Woodbridge, N.J.; San Francisco, Cal.; Baton Rouge, La.; and Cleveland, Ohio.

Reynolds owns a controlling interest in the Eskimo Pie Corp. which has a plant in Bloomfield, New Jersey.

(Reynolds Metals Company, continued)
Reynolds also owns 29.3% of the stock of Robertshaw Controls, producer of "Lux" clocks, "Minute Minder" timers, and diversified industrial controls. Offices of Robertshaw are in Richmond, Virginia.

SCOVILL MANUFACTURING COMPANY
99 Mill Street
Waterbury, Connecticut 06720
(203) 757–6061

MAJOR PRODUCTS:

Pins, air conditioners, appliances, basic metals, building materials

CONSUMER BRANDS:

Dominion, Hamilton Beach household appliances; *NuTone* built-in home fixtures; *Lightcraft* fixtures; *Caradco* windows; *Auricord* tape players; *Dritz* sewing aids; *Nyguard, Nylaire* zippers

FINANCIAL DATA:

$ Millions	1969	1968	1967
Net Sales	444.5	396.3	355.8
Net Income	15.6	14.5	12.7
P/E Ratio	14–10	16–8	15–11
Yr End Mkt Value	146.9		

ANTI-PERSONNEL CONTRACTS:

$4.2 million—metal parts for cluster bombs
1/69—$2.4 million for bomblet fuses
4/69—$1.5 million modification for bomblet fuses

OFFICERS AND DIRECTORS:

Chairman: Malcolm Baldrige, Woodbury, Connec-

(Scovill Manufacturing Company, continued)
ticut (Director: University of Connecticut Foundation, Inc., Maderia School, Yale University Development Board; Member Executive Comm., Director: Eastern Co., Lewis Engineering Co., Waterbury Savings Bank, Colonial Bank & Trust Co., American Chain & Cable Co., Conn. Mutual Life Ins. Co., Northeast Utilities, Swiss Reinsurance Co.)
President: John C. Helies

OUTSIDE DIRECTORS:

Andrew Gagarin: President, Torrington Mfg. Co.
Allen D. Marshall: President, United Students Air Fund
John A. Morgan: Chairman, Butler Mfg. Co.
Sherman R. Knapp: Chairman, Northeast Utilities
Daniel Davison: Vice-President, Morgan Guaranty Trust Co.
Mayo Shattuck: Partner, State Street Research & Mfg. Co.
Mark L. Sperry II: Retired Vice-President, Scovill Mfg. Co.

ANNUAL MEETING:

The annual meeting is held during April in Waterbury, Connecticut.

PLANTS:

Washington, Clinton and Wake Forest, N.C.; Cincinnati and Reading, Ohio; Los Angeles, Cal.; Bingham, Maine; Auburn, Neb.; Dubuque, Iowa, Pem-

(Scovill Manufacturing Company, continued)
berton, Newark and Caldwell, N.J.; Long Island
City, N.Y.; Oakville, Southington, Waterbury,
Thomaston and New Milford, Conn.; Fayetteville
and Dickson, Tenn.; Spartanburg, S.C.; Lebanon,
Pa.; Middleboro, Mass.; Montross and Victoria, Va.;
Manchester, N.H.; Clarkesville, Ga.; and Greenwood,
Miss.

Staylastic/Smith, Inc., a Scovill subsidiary, maintains
a plant at New Bedford, Mass.

The main office of Dominion Electric, a subsidiary
of Scovill, is in Mansfield, Ohio.

Sterling Industries, Inc., a subsidiary of Scovill Mfg.,
makes lighting fixtures, interior directional signs, and
commercial building markers at its plant in Philadelphia, Pa.

SPERRY RAND CORPORATION
1290 Avenue of the Americas
New York, New York 10019
(212) 956–2121

MAJOR PRODUCTS:

Instrumentation, navigation controls, business machines, shavers

CONSUMER BRANDS:

Remington office machines, shavers; *Univac* data processors

FINANCIAL DATA:

$ Millions	3/31/69*	1968	1967
Net Sales	1,607.3	1562.8	1487.1
Net Income	77.0	64.0	53.9
P/E Ratio	28–18	34–14	19–10
Yr End Mkt Value	1,263.0		

ANTI-PERSONNEL CONTRACTS:

$44.0 million to load, assemble and pack CBU–25A/A anti-personnel bombs, M151 2.75 inch rocket warheads and other ammunition for use in Southeast Asia

6/69–$28.3 million modification of above contract

* Sperry Rand's annual accounting period ends on March 31 of each calendar year.

166

(Sperry Rand Corporation, continued)
9/69—$1.9 million modification
10/69—$14.9 million modification

OFFICERS AND DIRECTORS:

Chairman/President: J. Frank Forster, New York, N.Y.

OUTSIDE DIRECTORS:

Norman Frost: Partner, Frost & Towers

Sherman Hazeltine: Chairman, First National Bank of Arizona

H. M. Jacob: President/Director, Inspiration Consolidated Copper Co.

Joseph H. King, Sr.: Partner, Eastman Dillon, Union Securities Co.

John F. Merriam: Former President/Chairman, Chairman Finance and Exec. Comm. and Director, Northern Natural Gas

Robert Slater: President/Director, John Hancock Life Insurance

Rupert C. Thompson: Chairman, Textron, Inc.

Harry F. Vickers: Former Chairman, Sperry Rand

ANNUAL MEETING:

The annual meeting of stockholders is held during July in New York City.

PLANTS:

Sperry Rand occupies 70 plants in 22 states. Research labs are located in Philadelphia, Pa.; St.

(Sperry Rand Corporation, continued)
Paul, Minn.; Troy, Mich.; Sudbury, Mass.; South
Norwalk, Conn.; Great Neck, N.Y.

Plants are in New Brunswick, N.J.; Elmira, Herkimer,
Tonowanda, North Tonowanda, Ilion, Utica, Long
Island City, Great Neck and Syossett, N.Y.; Mari-
etta, Ohio; Danville, Ill.; Boston, Mass.; Middle-
town and Bridgeport, Conn.; Menlo Park and
Fowler, Cal.; Searcy, Ark.; Des Moines, Iowa; Bris-
tol, Tenn.; Roseville, Minn.; Salt Lake City, Utah;
Clearwater and Gainesville, Fla.; Phoenix, Ariz.;
Charlottesville, Va.; New Holland and Belleville,
Pa.; Grand Island and Omaha, Neb.; Joplin, Mo.;
Jackson, Miss.; Durham, N.C.; and Tulsa, Okla.

STANDARD KOLLSMAN INDUSTRIES
2085 N. Hawthorne Avenue
Melrose Park, Illinois
(312) 344–5680

MAJOR PRODUCTS:

Aircraft instruments, optical equipment, fire extinguishers, television tuners, electronic switches, automobile accessories

CONSUMER BRANDS:

Standard Grigsby electric switches, *Lee-Der and Casco* fire extinguishers, *Nelmor* automobile mirrors, *Bobpro* electric blankets and heating pads, *Kollsman* instruments

FINANCIAL DATA:

$ Millions	1969	1968	1967
Net Sales	114.4	111.5	110.6
Net Income	.8	—.4	3.0
P/E Ratio	89–30		30–14

ANTI-PERSONNEL CONTRACTS:

[Contracts are held by Kollsman Instruments, a division of Standard Kollsman Industries]
10/67–$549,021 for M18 and M18A1 Claymore anti-personnel mines
6/68–$343,036 for M18 and M18A1 Claymore mines

(Standard Kollsman Industries, continued)

1/69—$597,844 for M18 and M18A1 Claymore mines

1/69—$2.5 million for firing devices for M57 anti-personnel mines

12/69—$1.1 million for metal parts for M18A1 Claymore mines

OFFICERS AND DIRECTORS:

Chairman: John B. Huarisa

President: Lloyd F. Taylor, Bridgeport, Connecticut

OUTSIDE DIRECTORS:

John P. Hoffmann: Senior Vice-President, Continental Illinois Bank and Trust Co.

Perry Addleman

W. McNeil Kennedy

Henry W. Meers: Partner, White Weld and Co.

James W. Burke

Richard K. Gottschall: Chairman, Atlas Chemical Co.

Thomas E. Magines

Gerald J. Wubbenhorst

ANNUAL MEETING:

The annual meeting of shareholders is held during May.

PLANT SITES:

Plants of the company and subsidiaries are operated in Melrose Park and Aurora, Illinois; Syosset, Westbury and Elmhurst, New York; Oshkosh, Wisconsin; Detroit, Michigan and Bridgeport, Connecticut.

SUSQUEHANNA CORPORATION
Alexandria, Virginia
(703) 354–4900

MAJOR PRODUCTS:

Propulsion systems, nuclear energy systems, uranium mining, building materials, ore processing

FINANCIAL DATA:

$ Millions	1969	1968	1967
Net Sales	129.7	140.5	132.3
Net Income	6.5	12.4	7.8
Yr End Mkt Value	40.8		

ANTI-PERSONNEL CONTRACTS:

[Atlantic Research holds the following contracts]
$9.0 million for XM3 anti-personnel mine dispensers
  Research and development on SUU–13/A dispensers
1/69—$1.1 million for 2.75 inch rocket motor igniters

[Flare Northern Division, West Hanover, Massachusetts, holds the following contracts]
FY 67—$3.0 million to develop and produce XM27 high explosive (H.E.) and chemical gravel mine; also XM47 mine dispenser
1967—$8.0 million for design, data, production equipment for XM41E1 mines

(Susquehanna Corporation, continued)
OFFICERS AND DIRECTORS:

Chairman: Arthur W. Sloan, Washington, D.C.
President: Herbert Korholz, Washington, D.C.
  (Chairman, Executive Committee: Pan American
  Sulphur Co.)

OUTSIDE DIRECTORS:

M. M. Hardin: Chairman, American Gypsum Co.
J. Earle May: Vice-President, Mitchum, Jones & Templeton, Inc.
Arch C. Scurlock: President, Research Industries, Inc.
Aksel Nielson: Chairman, Mortgage Investment Co.
D. W. Reeves: Chairman, Public Service Corp. of New Mexico

ANNUAL MEETING:

The annual meeting is held during April in Alexandria, Virginia.

PLANTS AND FACILITIES:

Susquehanna maintains regional offices in Chicago; Washington, D.C.; San Bernadino; Los Angeles; Parsippany, N.J.; Huntsville, Ala.; Dayton; Boston; Atlanta; Tucson.
Consolidated subsidiaries and their sites are:
Atlantic Research Corp.: Alexandria, Va.; Washington, D.C.; Fort Huachuca, Ariz.; Costa Mesa, Calif.; Green River, Utah; White Sands, N.M.; Gainesville,

(Susquehanna Corporation, continued)
Va.; Corolla, N.C.; Saugus, Cal.; West Hanover and Halifax, Mass.

American Gypsum, Inc.: Albuquerque, N.M.

Susquehanna-Western, Inc.: Falls City, Texas; Edgemont, S.D.; Riverton, Wyoming.

Maclin Co.: Los Angeles, Cal.

Mines Development, Inc.: Edgemont, S.D.

Crestlite, Inc.: San Clemente, Cal.

Mercator, Inc.: Denver, Colo.

Rockwell Premium Brand Div.: Pueblo, Colo.; Belton, Texas; Fontana, Cal.

R & G Sloane Mfg. Div.: Sun Valley, Cal.; W. Caldwell, N.J.; Valley View, Ohio; Atlanta, Ga.

Kelsey-Ferguson Brick Co.: E. Windsor Hill, Conn., and Middleboro, Mass.

United Perlite Corp.: Antonio, Colo.

Treesdale Labs Div.: Saxonburg, Pa.

Pittsburgh Metals Purifying Co.: Saxonburg, Pa.

Struh Process Steel Co.: Saxonburg, Pa.

Ingot-Aid Co.: New Castle, Pa.

The Waukegan-North Chicago Transit Co., a Susquehanna subsidiary, operates buses in northern Illinois.

Pan American Sulphur Co., a subsidiary of Susquehanna, operates as a holding company for affiliates engaged in exploration, development, and production of sulphur. It is located in Houston, Texas.

TYLER CORPORATION
(formerly Saturn Industries)
Southland Center
Dallas, Texas 75201
(214) 747–8251

MAJOR PRODUCTS:

Precision machine parts, helicopter sub-assemblies, electronic components, transportation

FINANCIAL DATA:

$ Millions	1969	1968	1967
Net Sales	134.7	104.2	60.3
Net Income	4.4	3.7	2.5
P/E Ratio	17–6	20–8	19–9
Yr End Mkt Value	33.3		

ANTI-PERSONNEL CONTRACTS:

[Contracts are held by Crescent Precision Products, a subsidiary of Tyler Industries]

10/66–$3.2 million for SUU–30/B "Sadeye" dispensers

$4.6 million for SUU–30B/B "Sadeye" dispensers and containers

3/68–$3.3 million for SUU–30B/B "Sadeye" dispensers and containers

9/68–$2.9 million for SUU–30B/B "Sadeye" dispensers and containers

3/69–$483,210 for SUU–30B/B "Sadeye" dispensers

(Tyler Corporation, continued)

10/69—$3.1 million for SUU–30B/B "Sadeye" dispensers

OFFICERS AND DIRECTORS:

Chairman: Joseph P. Driscoll, Dallas, Texas (Chairman: Lakeshore Apts., Inc., Community Water Service, Inc.)
President: Joseph F. McKinney

OUTSIDE DIRECTORS:

Ira G. Corn: Financial Consultant
Sam Labello, Jr.: Real estate investor
W. O. Harrington: Chairman, C & H Transportation Co.
Gilbert Anderson: President, Harbor Boat Building Co.
H. Clyde Mills: President, Crescent Precision Products
Howard Smith: President, C & H Transportation Co.
W. H. Graves: President, Saturn Electronics
Richard C. Memhard: President, Electronic Capital Corp.

ANNUAL MEETING:

The annual meeting of shareholders is customarily held during February in Dallas, Texas.

PLANTS AND SERVICES:

Tyler Corp. owns C & H Transportation of Dallas, Texas, the largest heavy hauler in the nation.

(Tyler Corporation, continued)
Crescent Precision Products is split into two divisions, Crescent-Dallas (formerly L. T. Industries) and Crescent-Tulsa.

Other Tyler subsidiaries are: Tyler Pipe Co., Saturn Electronics, Harbor Boat Building and Mitchell Industries.

UNIROYAL, INC.
1230 Avenue of the Americas
New York, New York 10020
(212) 247-5000

MAJOR PRODUCTS:

Rubber goods, naugahyde, sporting goods, apparel, agricultural products, retailing

CONSUMER BRANDS:

Uniroyal, Fisk tires; *Royal* golf equipment (Uniroyal is the world's leading producer of golf balls); *Keds* shoes; *Sunfish* and *Eskiloos* clothing; *Naugahyde*

FINANCIAL DATA:

	$ Millions	1969	1968	1967
Net Sales		1553.8	1429.2	1264.7
Net Income		46.6	56.9	33.0
P/E Ratio			16–10	22–16
Yr End Mkt Value		516.1		

ANTI-PERSONNEL CONTRACTS:

5/69—$7.1 million for explosives and loading, packing
 and assembling cluster bombs
9/69—$3.4 million contract modification on above
1/70—$13.7 million modification on above

OFFICERS AND DIRECTORS:

Chairman/President: George R. Vila, Far Hills, New

(Uniroyal, Inc., continued)
   Jersey (Director: ACF Industries, Chemical Bank
   of N.Y., National Industrial Conference Board;
   Trustee Emeritus, Wesleyan University)

OUTSIDE DIRECTORS:

Joseph W. Chinn, Jr.: Chairman, Wilmington Trust
   Co.
J. S. Dean: President, Nemours Corp.
Malcolm Ferguson: Past President, Director, Bendix
   Corp.
G. Arnold Hart: Chairman, Bank of Montreal
Harold Helm: Past Board Chairman, Chairman Exec.
   Comm. and Director, Chemical Bank of N.Y.
James P. Lewis: President, J. P. Lewis Co.
John W. McGovern: Former President, Uniroyal
Robert J. McKim: Former Chairman/President, Asso-
   ciated Dry Goods Corp.
John M. Schiff: Partner, Kuhn, Loeb & Co.
W. Dent Smith: Director, Canadian Corps.
Charles Spofford: Partner, Davis, Polk and Wardwell
Robert J. Tyson: Chairman Fin. Comm., U. S. Steel
Harvey G. Mehlhouse

ANNUAL MEETING:

The annual meeting is held during April in New York
City.

PLANTS AND FACILITIES:

Uniroyal maintains an increasing number of retail

(Uniroyal, Inc., continued)
outlets in shopping centers, the Uniroyal automotive
products stores.

Their research center is in Middlebury, Connecticut.

VICTOR COMPTOMETER CORPORATION
3900 North Rockwell Street
Chicago, Illinois 60618
(312) 539–8210

MAJOR PRODUCTS:

Business products and recreational equipment, temporary help agencies and business schools

CONSUMER BRANDS:

Heddon fishing equipment, *Daisy* rifles, *Bear* archery equipment, *Worthington, PGA* (these are the only golf balls endorsed by the P.G.A.), *CPGA* golf balls and golf equipment, *Victor* office machines, *Valley* billiard equipment *Tommy Armour, Chick Harbert, Bert Yancey, Jim Wiecher, Alice Bauer* golf clubs, *Ertl* toys, *Comptometer* office machines

FINANCIAL DATA:

	$ Millions	1969	1968	1967
Net Sales		161.6	153.9	144.2
Net Income		9.0	9.2	11.2
P/E Ratio		37–15	51–25	43–21
Yr End Mkt Value		148.9		

ANTI-PERSONNEL CONTRACTS:

$2.2 million for BLU–26 "guava" steel balls

$456,000 for BLU–26/B and BLU–59/B carbon steel balls

$1.0 million for steel balls for bomblets

(Victor Comptometer Corporation, continued)

OFFICERS AND DIRECTORS:

Chairman: Albert C. Buehler, Barrington, Illinois
President: Alvin F. Bakwell

OUTSIDE DIRECTORS:

Carl Buehler (son of Albert): Chairman of the Board, Victor Comptometer Ltd.
E. M. Cummings: Vice-President, Continental Illinois Bank & Trust Co.
Lloyd Drexler: Executive Vice-President, Allied Products Co.
Harold P. O'Connell: Retired banker
Cass S. Hough: President/Director, Daisy/Heddon Group

ANNUAL MEETING:

The annual meeting is customarily held during January in Chicago.

PLANTS AND SERVICES:

Maintains plants in Lincoln, Neb.; Merced, Cal.; Atlanta, Georgia; Arlington, Texas; Nashville, Tenn.; Rogers, Ark.; Elyria, Ohio; Kalamazoo and Grayling, Mich.; Chicago and Morton Grove, Ill.; Dyersville and Des Moines, Iowa.

Victor business schools and Victor temporary help agencies are located in many large cities.

Research labs are in Des Plaines, Iowa and West Hartford, Conn.

WHIRLPOOL CORPORATION
Benton Harbor, Michigan 49023
(616) 925–0651

MAJOR PRODUCTS:

Home appliances, consumer products, defense work

CONSUMER BRANDS:

Whirlpool, Kenmore, Coldspot home appliances; *Thomas* organs

FINANCIAL DATA:

$ Millions	1969	1968	1967
Net Sales	1,153.5	825.8	773.7
Net Income	45.9	36.2	33.3
P/E Ratio		21–15	20–11
Yr End Mkt Value	694.4		

ANTI-PERSONNEL CONTRACTS:

Design and development of new and improved flechettes and applicable weapons systems
$5.1 million for 105mm Beehive projectiles

OFFICERS AND DIRECTORS:

Chairman: E. Gray II, Benton Harbor, Michigan
(Chairman: Warwick Electronics; Director: Sears
Bank & Trust Co., General Foods Corp.; Member:
M.I.T. Corp.; Trustee: University of Evansville)
President: J. H. Platts, St. Joseph, Michigan

(Whirlpool Corporation, continued)

OUTSIDE DIRECTORS:

S. L. Boyar: Vice-President, Sears, Roebuck

C. W. Cook: President, General Foods

H. S. Eberhard: Former Chairman, Caterpillar Tractor Co.

N. E. Halaby: President, Pan Am World Airways

J. S. Holl: Chairman, Dayton Rogers Mfg. Co.

F. R. Kappel: Chairman, International Paper

B. C. Murch: President/Treasurer, Murch & Co., Inc.

ANNUAL MEETING:

The annual meeting is held during April in Benton Harbor, Michigan.

PLANTS:

Whirlpool maintains plants in Clyde, Marion and Findlay, Ohio; Evansville, Ill.; Ft. Smith, Ark.; St. Joseph, Mich.; St. Paul, Minn.; LaPort, Ind.; and Sunnyvale, Cal.

Heil-Quaker subsidiary maintains a plant in Lewisburg, Tenn.

Warwick Electronics and its subsidiary, Thomas Organs, maintain plants in Chicago, Evanston and Zion, Ill.; Covington, Tenn.; Forrest City, Ark.; Saginaw, Mich.; Niles, Ill.; Sepulveda, Cal.

WHITTAKER CORPORATION
9229 Sunset Boulevard
Los Angeles, California 90069
(213) 274–0771

MAJOR PRODUCTS:

Structural materials, metal alloy products, government contracts (33% of sales; 87% of these are for Department of Defense)

CONSUMER BRANDS:

Columbia, Coronado, Bertram, Trojan, Kettenberg yachts, *Courier, Fanon* CB radios, *Universal* gym equipment, *Bunting* furniture

FINANCIAL DATA:

$ Millions	1969	1968	1967
Net Sales	753.4	614.1	381.6
Net Income	30.7	22.7	15.7
P/E Ratio	22–10	32–20	58–8
Yr End Mkt Value	223.2		

ANTI-PERSONNEL CONTRACTS:

$2.4 million for igniters for 2.75 inch rocket motors
10/68—$19.0 million for BLU–24/B and BLU–66/B
  bomb components
11/69—$2.9 million for 2.75 inch rocket motor igniters
$83,520 for nozzle assemblies for 2.75 inch rockets

(Whittaker Corporation, continued)

OFFICERS AND DIRECTORS:

Chairman: William R. Whittaker, Los Angeles, California

President: William M. Duke, Encino, California (Chairman: Computing & Software, Inc.)

OUTSIDE DIRECTORS:

Glenn G. Havens: President, Havens Industries, Inc.
Richard E. Krafve: Management Consultant
Leo A. Pfankuch: President, Servisoft of Riverside

ANNUAL MEETING:

The annual meeting is customarily held during March in the Santa Monica Civic Auditorium, Santa Monica, California.

PLANTS:

Whittaker plants are in La Mesa, Monrovia, Costa Mesa, Los Angeles, North Hollywood, San Diego and Van Nuys, Cal. and Denver, Colo. Corporate research facilities are in San Diego, Cal.
Universal Athletic has a plant in Fresno, Cal.
Dynasciences Corp. has facilities in Chatsworth, Los Angeles, North Hollywood and Pasadena, Cal.; Bethesda and Walkersville, Md.; and Blue Bell, Pa.
Trojan Yacht Co. has plants in Elkton, Md.; Intercourse, Kinzer and Lancaster, Pa.
Columbia Yacht Co. has plants in Costa Mesa, Cal. and Portsmouth, Va.

(Whittaker Corporation, continued)

Coronado Yacht Co. has a plant in Costa Mesa, Cal.

Kettenberg Marine is located in San Diego and Santa Monica, Cal.

Bertram Yacht is located in Miami, Fla.

Marine Hardware Inc. is located in Newport Beach and San Pedro, Cal.

Crown Aluminum Corp. has plants in Stanton, Del.; Arlington Heights, Ill.; Indianapolis, Ind.; Beltsville, Md.; Livonia, Mich.; Palisades Pk., N.J.; Chili, Poughkeepsie, Syracuse, Utica and Vestal, N.Y.; Columbia and Valley View, Ohio; Pittsburgh, Pa.

Mercer Alloys has plants in Melrose, Ill. and Warren, Ohio

Other Whittaker subsidiaries are located in Ala., Cal., Colo., Fla., Ga., Ill., Ind., Kans., La., Md., Mass., Minn., Nev., N.J., N.M., N.Y., N.C., Ohio, Okla., Pa., R.I., Texas.

CORPORATE POSTURE:

"Profit margins in this area [Architectural Products Group] are below those of the company as a whole, largely due to the adverse affect of Vietnam on volume which put a damper on potential economies of scale. Management estimates revenues in this group could reach $100 million (Sales were $38–40 million in 1968) shortly after a cessation of hostilities.

". . . Although Vietnam-oriented products such as flares, ordnance igniters and jet-assistance take-off units comprise 20% of the Technical Products Group's

(Whittaker Corporation, continued)

sales, deferred and reactivated cancelled programs would eventually offset any decline due to the war's end." From *The Wall St. Transcript*, June 17, 1968.

WURLITZER COMPANY
105 West Adams Street
Chicago, Illinois 60603
(312) 263–3373

MAJOR PRODUCTS:

Musical instruments, phonographs, jukeboxes, retailing, defense products (11% of sales)

CONSUMER BRANDS:

Martin, Wurlitzer musical instruments and jukeboxes

FINANCIAL DATA:

$ Millions	3/31/69*	1968	1967
Net Sales	61.0	59.9	57.3
Net Income	2.2	2.0	2.1
P/E Ratio	15–11	22–11	17–9
Yr End Mkt Value	15.9		

ANTI-PERSONNEL CONTRACTS:

$546,566—power supply for XM429 electronic proximity fuses for 2.75 inch rockets

OFFICERS AND DIRECTORS:

Chairman: R. C. Rolfing, Wilmette, Illinois (Chairman: Summers & Son, Inc.)

* Wurlitzer's annual accounting period ends on March 31 of each calendar year.

(Wurlitzer Company, continued)

President: W. N. Herleman, Sycamore, Illinois (Director, First Savings and Loan of Sycamore)

OUTSIDE DIRECTORS:

R. C. Liddon: Chairman, Security Bank of Corinth, Miss.

James M. Hutton III: Vice-President/Director, W. E. Hutton Corp.

William G. Olson: Vice-President, Continental Illinois National Bank

ANNUAL MEETING:

The annual meeting is held during June in Chicago.

PLANTS:

Wurlitzer has manufacturing facilities in DeKalb, Ill.; Corinth and Holly Springs, Miss.; North Tonawanda, N.Y.; and Elkhart, Ind. They also maintain 38 retail outlets.

On March 27, 1970, Wurlitzer announced plans to build a new plant in Logan, Utah. Completion is expected in late 1971.

ZENITH RADIO CORPORATION
1900 North Austin Avenue
Chicago, Illinois 60639
(312) 745–2000

MAJOR PRODUCTS:

Radios and TV sets and equipment, picture tubes, defense products: proximity fuses and safety-arming devices

CONSUMER BRANDS:

Zenith radio and TV products, phonographs and components, hearing aids

FINANCIAL DATA:

$ Millions	1969	1968	1967
Net Sales	676.6	705.4	653.9
Net Income	39.6	47.3	41.0
P/E Ratio		26–20	33–22
Yr End Mkt Value	627.6		

ANTI-PERSONNEL CONTRACTS:

$4.7 million for M429 electronic proximity fuses for 2.75 inch rockets

2/69—$2.1 million for contract modification on above contracts

11/69—$1.1 million modification on above contract

OFFICERS AND DIRECTORS:

Chairman and President: Joseph S. Wright, Kenil-

(Zenith Radio Corporation, continued)
worth, Illinois (Director: Rauland Corp., Continental Illinois Bank & Trust Co., Standard Oil of Indiana; Trustee: University of Chicago)

OUTSIDE DIRECTORS:

Thomas G. Ayers: President, Commonwealth Edison

Edward F. Blettner: President/Director, First National Bank of Chicago

Hugh Robertson: Honorary Chairman

Karl E. Hassell: Assistant Vice-President, Zenith Radio

W. S. Woodfill: Chairman/Owner, Grand Hotel of Mackinac Island

E. N. Rauland: President/Director, Rauland Corp.

Hays MacFarland: Chairman Exec. Comm., Earle Ludgin & Co.

ANNUAL MEETING:

The annual meeting is held during April in Chicago.

PLANTS:

Zenith maintains plants in Chicago, Illinois; Springfield, Mo., and Sioux City, Iowa.

The Rauland Division has plants in Chicago, Niles, Melrose Park and Melrose, Illinois.

Corporate research center is in Menlo Park, California.

AAI CORPORATION*/ Baltimore, Maryland (Research and development of anti-personnel weapons was done at the Cockeysville, Maryland facility.)

MAJOR PRODUCTS:

Electronic ordnance systems

ANTI-PERSONNEL CONTRACTS:

Design and development of XM617U anti-personnel mine fuse (joint project with United Aerotest Labs)

Design and development of the special purpose individual weapon (SPIW) for firing Beehive and flechette projectiles

ABG INSTRUMENT AND ENGINEERING CORP./ Santa Barbara, California

ANTI-PERSONNEL CONTRACTS:

FY 68—$251,220 for lockwires for 2.75 inch rockets

ACF INDUSTRIES, INC./ New York City (Anti-personnel weapons were produced at the St. Louis, Missouri plant)

---

* 84% of the stock of AAI Corp is owned by United Industrial Corp. of New York City, a manufacturer of hospital supplies and military weaponry.

MAJOR PRODUCTS:

Railroad cars, automobile equipment

CONSUMER BRANDS:

Carter carburetors, fuel pumps and filters, smog control devices

ANTI-PERSONNEL CONTRACTS:

FY 66—$4.1 million for metal parts for cluster bombs

ADVENTURE LINE MANUFACTURING CO./ *Parsons, Kansas*

MAJOR PRODUCTS:

Die cast aluminum products

ANTI-PERSONNEL CONTRACTS:

12/68—$3.3 million for metal parts for BLU–26/B "guava" bombs

AERONCA, INC./ *Middletown, Ohio*

MAJOR PRODUCTS:

Aerospace products

ANTI-PERSONNEL CONTRACTS:

12/66—$371,651 for XM3 mine dispensers
  8/67—$490,215 for XM3 mine dispensers

11/67—$ 70,851 for XM3 mine dispensers
 3/68—$334,373 for XM3 mine dispensers
 5/68—$318,507 for XM3 mine dispensers
$1.0 million for parts for XM3 mine dispensers
$86,600 for XM3 production engineering
$114,949 for XM3 shell assembly
$73,080 for assembly of XM17 mines

AIRPORT MACHINING CORP./ Martin, Tennessee

ANTI-PERSONNEL CONTRACTS:

FY 68—$3.5 million for M151 warheads for 2.75 inch rockets
4/69—$3.1 million for warheads for 2.75 inch rockets
11/69—$1.1 million for warheads for 2.75 inch rockets
3/70—$1.7 million for warheads for 2.75 inch rockets

AJAX HARDWARE MANUFACTURING CO./ City of Industry, California

MAJOR PRODUCTS:

Industrial hardware

ANTI-PERSONNEL CONTRACTS:

3/69—$135,000 for parts for BLU–26/B "guava" bomblets

ALADDIN HEATING CO./ San Leandro, California

MAJOR PRODUCTS:

Blowers, furnaces

ANTI-PERSONNEL CONTRACTS:

5/69–$197,600 for refurbishment of CNU–80/E25 containers and related data applicable to SUU–14/A and SUU–14A/A

AMERICAN MANUFACTURING CO. OF TEXAS/ Fort Worth, Texas

ANTI-PERSONNEL CONTRACTS:

$1.0 million for M151 warheads for 2.75 inch rockets

AMERICAN STANDARD, INC./ New York City (Contracts are held by Melpar Division, of Columbus, Ohio)

MAJOR PRODUCTS:

Building materials, plumbing products

CONSUMER BRANDS:

Standard toilets, air conditioners

ANTI-PERSONNEL CONTRACTS:

Development of Rockeye II dispenser fuses

*AMETEK, INC./ New York City (Anti-person-
nel weapons were produced at the Sheboygan,
Wisconsin plant)*

MAJOR PRODUCTS:

Testing and measuring instruments, coin-operated
laundry machines, missile components

ANTI-PERSONNEL CONTRACTS:

$1.5 million for stabilizer rods for 2.75 inch rockets
11/69–$1.1 million for stabilizer rods for 2.75 inch
rockets

*BACHE TOOL AND DIE CO. (CONCEPT
INDUSTRIES)/ Westbury, New York*

MAJOR PRODUCTS:

Formed metal, small machined parts

ANTI-PERSONNEL CONTRACTS:

2/69–$217,259 for CBU–24/29 bomb bodies
$260,252 for parts for BLU–26/B "guava" bomblets

*BEMIS CO./ Minneapolis, Minnesota (Anti-
personnel weapons research was done at the
Hicksville, New York facility of Perry Industries, a subsidiary of Bemis Co.)*

MAJOR PRODUCTS:

Paper, plastics, textiles

ANTI-PERSONNEL CONTRACTS:

$233,987 for development of loading machinery for XM-45E1 anti-personnel mines

BIRMA PRODUCTS/ Sayresville, New Jersey

ANTI-PERSONNEL CONTRACTS:

FY 69—$159,807 for parts for 2.75 inch rockets

BREED CORP./ Fairfield, New Jersey

ANTI-PERSONNEL CONTRACTS:

FY 69—$750,000 for design and development of XM43 anti-personnel mine and sub-pack system

C & S BALL BEARING MACHINERY AND EQUIPMENT CORP. OF AMERICA/ Meridian, Connecticut

MAJOR PRODUCTS:

Bearings, precision metal balls

ANTI-PERSONNEL CONTRACTS:

1/69—$228,000 for carbon steel balls for CBU–24/29/49 bomblets
10/69—$160,640 for carbon steel balls for CBU–24/49 bomblets
$57,000 for carbon steel balls for CBU–24/49 bomblets

CHAMBERLAIN MANUFACTURING CO./ *Elmhurst, Illinois (Anti-personnel weapons are produced at the Waterloo, Iowa plant)*

MAJOR PRODUCTS:

Ordnance items, aluminum home products

CONSUMER BRANDS:

Chambron home improvement products, *Ampli-Vox* and *Perma-Power* sound systems

ANTI-PERSONNEL CONTRACTS:

11/69–$1.0 million for metal parts for 2.75 inch rocket warheads
FY 69–$1.0 million for 2.75 inch rocket warheads
3/70–$1.6 million for 2.75 inch rocket warheads

CORNELL AERONAUTICAL LABS.*/*Buffalo, New York*

MAJOR PRODUCTS:

Scientific research

ANTI-PERSONNEL CONTRACTS:

1/69–$39,823 for anti-disturbance module development for M18 anti-personnel mine

* On March 4, 1970, the New York Supreme Court ruled that EDP Technology could not buy Cornell Aeronautical Labs. from Cornell University. In his opinion, Justice Harold P. Kelly ruled, "The gift to Cornell of Cornell Aeronautical Labs was a charitable gift restricted to the purpose of conducting research for the public interest or benefit."

DAY AND ZIMMERMAN/ *Philadelphia, Pennsylvania*

ANTI-PERSONNEL CONTRACTS:

$99,219,021 for loading and packing 2.75 inch rockets and other munitions

DIODES, INC./ *Chatsworth, California (Research for anti-personnel weapons was done at Horsham, Pennsylvania plant of Microcom, Inc., a subsidiary of Diodes, Inc.)*

MAJOR PRODUCTS:

Silicon semi-conductors

ANTI-PERSONNEL CONTRACTS:

FY 68—$92,818 for development of telemetry systems for XM429 proximity fuses for 2.75 inch rockets

DOUGLAS AND LOMASON CO./ *Columbus, Ohio*

MAJOR PRODUCTS:

Automobile parts, ammunition parts

ANTI-PERSONNEL CONTRACTS:

12/68—$950,808 for M41A2 and M1A4 fragmentation bomb adapters
1/69—$1.3 million for fragmentation bombs and adapter clusters

FILTERS, INC./ San Jose, California

ANTI-PERSONNEL CONTRACTS:

FY 69—$163,395 for metal parts for 2.75 inch rockets

FRANKLIN INSTITUTE/ Philadelphia, Pennsylvania

MAJOR PRODUCTS:

Research

ANTI-PERSONNEL CONTRACTS:

1/67—$75,708 for support studies for button bomblets

GENTZLER TOOL AND DIE CORP./ Greensburg, Ohio

MAJOR PRODUCTS:

Formed metal parts

ANTI-PERSONNEL CONTRACTS:

2/69—$221,099 for CBU–24/49 crimp straps

GIBBS DIE CASTING ALUMINUM CORP./ Henderson, Kentucky

MAJOR PRODUCTS:

Cast aluminum hardware

ANTI-PERSONNEL CONTRACTS:

1/69—$1.5 million for BLU–26/B "guava" bomblets

HOOVER BALL AND BEARING CO./ *Ann Arbor, Michigan (Anti-personnel weapons were produced at the Erwin, Tennessee plant of the corporation)*

MAJOR PRODUCTS:

Precision metal balls

CONSUMER BRANDS:

Draw-Tite trailer hitches, *Omni* furniture, *Hoover* chrome-plated household fixtures

ANTI-PERSONNEL CONTRACTS:

1/69—$287,040 for CBU–24/29 steel balls
4/69—$221,040 for CBU–24/49 steel balls
$825,600 for CBU–24/49 steel balls

KELSEY-HAYES CO./ *Romulus, Michigan (Anti-personnel weapons were produced at the Philadelphia, Pennsylvania plant.)*

MAJOR PRODUCTS:

Truck and car wheels, aerospace equipment

CONSUMER BRANDS:

Kelsey custom automobile wheels

ANTI-PERSONNEL CONTRACTS:

$1.0 million for warheads for 2.75 inch rockets

KILIAN STEEL BALL CORP./ Hartford, Connecticut

MAJOR PRODUCTS:

Precision metal balls

ANTI-PERSONNEL CONTRACTS:

10/69—$564,186 for CBU–24/49 steel balls
$200,916 for CBU–24/49 steel balls

KOEHLER AND SONS/ Hatboro, Pennsylvania

ANTI-PERSONNEL CONTRACTS:

FY 68—$899,000 for steel balls for bomblets
1/69—$938,000 for steel balls and data for CBU–24/29/49 bomblets
4/69—$648,000 for steel balls for CBU–24/49

LANSDOWNE STEEL AND IRON CO./ Morton, Pennsylvania

MAJOR PRODUCTS:

Hollow steel forgings, textile machinery

ANTI-PERSONNEL CONTRACTS:

FY 68—$8.2 million for Mk56 anti-personnel projectiles

LASKO METAL PRODUCTS/ *Westchester, Pennsylvania*

CONSUMER BRANDS:

Lasko fans

ANTI-PERSONNEL CONTRACTS:

9/68—$3.3 million for SUU–14A/A
4/69—$29,671 for SUU–14/A
2/70—$2.9 million for SUU–14A/A bomblet dispensers

LEHIGH, INC./ *Easton, Pennsylvania*

MAJOR PRODUCTS:

Pneumatic valves, ferrous castings, commercial refrigeration equipment

ANTI-PERSONNEL CONTRACTS:

FY 68—$3.2 million for M229 warheads for 2.75 inch rockets

LOWENTHAL MANUFACTURING CO./ *Chicago, Illinois*

MAJOR PRODUCTS:

Industrial and custom sewing, vulcanized fiber cases

ANTI-PERSONNEL CONTRACTS:

FY 66—$383,332 for inner housings for XM22 gravel mines

SILAS MASON CO., INC (MASON AND HANGER)/ New York City

MAJOR PRODUCTS:

Engineering services

ANTI-PERSONNEL CONTRACTS:

$13,695,852 for operation of Iowa Army Ammunition Plant for production of gravel mines

MEDICO INDUSTRIES/ Wilkes-Barre, Pennsylvania

ANTI-PERSONNEL CONTRACTS:

FY 68—$4.0 million for M229 warheads for 2.75 inch rockets
$3.1 million for M151 warheads for 2.75 inch rockets

MILLER RESEARCH/ Baltimore, Maryland

ANTI-PERSONNEL CONTRACTS:

FY 68—$288,308 for development of a counter-ambush barrage system

NASH-HAMMOND, INC.

ANTI-PERSONNEL CONTRACTS:

1/68—$1.2 million for plastic canisters for Tactical Fighter Dispenser Munition

NEW PROCESS FIBER CO./ *Greenwood, Delaware*

MAJOR PRODUCTS:

Chemical fibers

ANTI-PERSONNEL CONTRACTS:

XM41 anti-personnel mine components

REPUBLIC CORP./ *Scranton, Pennsylvania*

MAJOR PRODUCTS:

Commercial film developing, minibikes, plastic disposable serving dishes, brown plastic bottles, outdoor furniture

CONSUMER BRANDS:

Republic mini-bikes; *Mar-Vel* welcome mats, electric fireplaces, plastic giftware

ANTI-PERSONNEL CONTRACTS:

9/67—$542,340 for M18 and M18A1 Claymore anti-
personnel mines
2/68—$237,125 for M18 and M18A1 Claymore anti-
personnel mines
1/69—$804,000 for M18 and M18A1 Claymore anti-
personnel mines

M. C. RICCIARDI/ *Alpha, New Jersey*

ANTI-PERSONNEL CONTRACTS:

11/69—$1.4 million for fibre containers for 2.75 inch rocket assemblies

RIKER-MAXSON CORP./ *New York City (Anti-personnel weapons work was done at the Macon, Georgia plant of Maxson Electronics, a division of Riker-Maxson)*

MAJOR PRODUCTS:

TV systems, electronic testing machines

ANTI-PERSONNEL CONTRACTS:

FY 68—$216,433 for XM429 proximity fuse testers

ROCKET RESEARCH CORP./ *Seattle, Washington (Research for anti-personnel weapons was done at the Issaquah, Wisconsin plant of Explosives Corp. of America, a subsidiary of Rocket Research)*

MAJOR PRODUCTS:

Rocket thrust equipment

ANTI-PERSONNEL CONTRACTS:

9/68—$172,483 for research and development for anti-personnel mines

2/69—Research and development for scatterable mines

ROIS MANUFACTURING CO./ *Philadelphia, Pennsylvania*

ANTI-PERSONNEL CONTRACTS:

2/69—$178,360 for M158A1 2.75 inch rocket launchers

RUBBERMAID INC./ *Wooster, Ohio (Fusion Rubbermaid, a subsidiary of Rubbermaid Inc., holds the anti-personnel contracts)*

MAJOR PRODUCTS:

Household articles, automobile accessories

CONSUMER BRANDS:

Rubbermaid household articles

ANTI-PERSONNEL CONTRACTS:

1/68—$1.4 million for plastic canisters for Tactical Fighter Dispenser Munition

SKAGIT CORP./ *Sedro-Wooley, Washington*

MAJOR PRODUCTS:

Hoists, winches

ANTI-PERSONNEL CONTRACTS:

$265,825 for M94B1 cartridges for 105mm flechette projectiles

SOUTHEASTERN DISTRIBUTING CO./ *Whitman, Massachusetts*

ANTI-PERSONNEL CONTRACTS:

FY 66—$407,029 for inner housings for XM22 gravel mines

FY 68—$246,500 for inner/outer housings for XM41E1 anti-personnel mines

STANDARD OIL COMPANY *(New Jersey)/ New York City (Research for anti-personnel weapons was done at the Linden, New Jersey facility of the Esso Research and Engineering Company, a subsidiary of Standard Oil)*

MAJOR PRODUCTS:

Exploration, production, and marketing of petroleum products

CONSUMER BRANDS:

Esso, Enco and *Humble* petroleum products and services

ANTI-PERSONNEL CONTRACTS:

Gravel mine sensitivity studies

STANFORD RESEARCH INSTITUTE/ *Menlo Park, California*

MAJOR PRODUCTS:

Scientific research

Anti-Personnel Contracts:

$87,950 for fragmentation warhead study

STERLING COMMERCIAL STEEL BALL CORP./ *Sterling, Illinois*

Major Products:

Precision metal balls

Anti-Personnel Contracts:

1/69–$177,480 for steel balls for CBU–24/49 cluster bombs

$675,500 for steel balls for CBU–24/29/49 cluster bombs

10/69–$426,000 for steel balls for CBU–24/29/49

$168,875 for steel balls for CBU–24/49 cluster bombs

SUPERIOR STEEL BALL CO./ *New Britain, Connecticut*

Major Products:

Precision metal balls

Anti-Personnel Contracts:

FY 68–$2.9 million for steel balls for BLU–26 "guava" bomblets

12/68–$2.3 million for BLU–26 "guava" components

1/69–$1.4 million for BLU–26 "guava" components

3/70–$1.5 million for components for anti-personnel bombs

TELEDYNE CORP./ Los Angeles, California (Anti-personnel contracts were held by Brown Engineering, a subsidiary of Teledyne)

MAJOR PRODUCTS:

Electronics, aviation control systems, oceanographical research

CONSUMER BRANDS:

Packard Bell TV sets

ANTI-PERSONNEL CONTRACTS:

11/67—$187,440 for M158 launchers for 2.75 inch rockets

TEMCO, INC./ Nashville, Tennessee (Anti-personnel weapons are produced at the Cullman, Alabama plant of Cullman Metalcraft, a subsidiary of Temco, Inc.)

MAJOR PRODUCTS:

Gas heating and commercial laundry equipment

ANTI-PERSONNEL CONTRACTS:

1/68—$302,580 for SUU–30B/B "Sadeye" dispensers and containers
9/68—$2.6 million for SUU–30B/B "Sadeye" dispensers and containers
12/68—$356,820 for SUU–30B/B "Sadeye" dispensers
3/69—$3.3 million for SUU–30B/B "Sadeye" dispensers

THIOKOL CHEMICAL CORP.*/ Bristol, Pennsylvania

MAJOR PRODUCTS:

Sprayers, kitchen cabinets, aerospace products, chemicals, vehicles

CONSUMER BRANDS:

Antonio Century ceramic tile; *Imp, Sprite, Rangemaster, Sno-Packer, Packmaster* and *Juggernaut* off-the-road vehicles

ANTI-PERSONNEL CONTRACTS:

FY 68—$189,739 for design and development of gravel mine sterilization system

FY 68—$537,730 for development of a chemical fuse for anti-personnel mines

TRENTON TEXTILE ENGINEERING AND MANUFACTURING CO./ Trenton, New Jersey

ANTI-PERSONNEL CONTRACTS:

FY 66—$234,808 for inner housings for XM22 gravel mines

---

* Thiokol is also active in the field of economic development. They operate a Job Corps center in Clearfield, Utah, a training center for adult American Indians in Roswell, New Mexico, and an occupational training facility for women in Atlanta, Georgia. They have also trained Peace Corps volunteers at their Utah facility.

FY 68—$25,000 initial letter contract on XM41 anti-personnel mines

$228,900 for inner/outer housings for XM41E1 anti-personnel mines

Components for XM45E1 mines

UNITED AEROTEST LABS, INC./ Deer Park, New York

ANTI-PERSONNEL CONTRACTS:

Development of fuse for XM617U anti-personnel mine (joint effort with AAI Corp.)

VIZ MANUFACTURING CO./ Philadelphia, Pennsylvania

MAJOR PRODUCTS:

Electronic recording devices

ANTI-PERSONNEL CONTRACTS:

7/68—$701,760 for XM57 anti-personnel mine components

WATERBURY STEEL BALL CO./ Waterbury, Connecticut

MAJOR PRODUCTS:

Precision metal balls

ANTI-PERSONNEL CONTRACTS:

1/69—$73,800 for steel balls for CBU–24/49 cluster bombs

WESTINGHOUSE ELECTRIC CO./ Pittsburgh, Pennsylvania

MAJOR PRODUCTS:

Electrical equipment, home appliances, TV stations, elevators

CONSUMER BRANDS:

Westinghouse appliances, *Group* W TV stations

ANTI-PERSONNEL CONTRACTS:

FY 67—$50,000 for integrated circuits for 2.75 inch rockets

Appendix

Other Conventional Weapons
Which Have Been Developed
or Converted for
Use in Vietnam

First in the list of these weapons are the Gatling-like 7.62mm Miniguns which are capable of firing 6,000 rounds of ammunition per minute. They are made by General Electric.[1] These guns are used in Huey helicopters which the Vietcong have nicknamed "The Muttering Death."[2] They are also used in Douglas AC-47s which were known as "Gooneybirds" during World War II. They have been converted for usage in the war in Vietnam by adding three side-firing Miniguns and are thus capable of firing 18,000 rounds of 7.62mm ammunition per minute. C. M. Plattner, of *Aviation Week and Space Technology*, tells of the new nickname of the AC-47's:

1. *Ordnance*, March–April, 1967, p. 482.
2. Harvey, *Air War: Vietnam*, p. 36.

Its high rate of fire and roar of the guns earned it the nickname of "Puff, the Magic Dragon."[3]

John T. Wheeler, a reporter for the St. Louis *Post Dispatch*, described the effectiveness of "Puff" on November 24, 1965:

Primarily an anti-personnel weapon, Puff circles a beleaguered enemy outpost while the pilot lines up the target in a gunsight pointed out of the left window. Flying at 122 knots, he fires while he keeps the left wing low and the pipper (illuminated sighting image) on the target . . . . Capable of circling long hours over a beleaguered fort or outpost, Puff can start the deadly circle quickly and in three seconds cover an area the size of a football field with at least one bullet to every square foot.

Not completely satisfied with that amount of power the Pentagon completed a contract with Fairchild-Hiller in 1968 to convert some C-119's for the same usage. These are to have four Miniguns, thus increasing the firing power to 24,000 rounds per minute.[4]

Defoliation is another form of warfare that the U. S. forces have developed. Since 1961, U. S. forces

3. C. M. Plattner, "Limited-War Concepts Weighed in Battle," *Aviation Week and Space Technology*, January 31, 1966, p. 42.

4. *Ordnance*, May–June, 1968, p. 532.

have been using chemical sprays to defoliate trees and brush in South Vietnam. (There is an excellent article on defoliation in the February 2, 1970 issue of *The New Yorker* by Thomas Whiteside). Defoliation is carried out by the Air Force under the code name Operation Ranch Hand. They fly Fairchild-Hiller C-123 Providers that have been adapted for spraying herbicides. The motto of Operation Ranch Hand is "Remember only you can prevent forests."[5]

The intention of this tactic was to deny the Vietcong the protection afforded by the foliage and thus to prevent ambushes of South Vietnamese and allied forces. In addition, defoliants have been used on rice fields in order to deny sources of food supply to the Vietcong. Defoliation was relatively successful in achieving these goals. By the end of 1969, about 12% of the land area in South Vietnam, which is about the size of the state of Massachusetts, had been sprayed with defoliants.

However, defoliation has had some additional adverse effects on the ecology of the Vietnamese countryside. The most powerful herbicides are 2,4-dichlorophenoxyacetic acid (known as 2,4-D) and 2,4,5-trichlorophenoxyacetic acid (known as 2,4,5-T). Where they have been used they have been responsible for extensive destruction of most plant life and this has upset the ecology of entire areas. The effects

5. Harvey, *Air War: Vietnam*, p. 39 and *Aviation Week and Space Technology*, May 8, 1967, p. 85. The latter issue has a series of color photographs of defoliation operations in South Vietnam.

may last for decades. Animals that were dependent on those plants for food will either die or no longer be able to live there. The soil that depends on fertilization by those plants will suffer. There is additional evidence that the defoliants have led to birth defects in Vietnamese children.[6] Professor Arthur Galston, Director of the Division of Biological Sciences of Yale University, has said that this destruction of the ecology of South Vietnam through the use of defoliants amounts to "environmental warfare."[7] Professor Galston wondered whether the United States was committing "ecocide" in South Vietnam, which would seem ironic in a country that we are supposed to be saving.

One more weapon that we have used extensively in Vietnam is napalm. The effects and usages of napalm have been well documented in the press: it is a burning agent and it is very effective against the enemy. It can be used to force personnel out into the open where they will then be subject to further air attack. Alternatively, napalm, because it consumes oxygen quickly, can be used to suffocate enemy personnel hidden in underground tunnels.

In addition, U. S. forces since 1965 have been using various gases in Vietnam to facilitate combat operations. Among those used are: DM, CN, and CS. All of these are improved tear gases which have been

6. Thomas Whiteside, "Reporter at Large," *The New Yorker,* February 2, 1970. Now available in paperback from Ballantine Books.

7. Congressional Conference on War and National Responsibility, February 20 and 21, 1970.

developed in recent years.[8] DM and CS also cause vomiting. President Nixon announced in November 1969 that the United States was renouncing the use of chemical and biological warfare. However, he did not include these gases in the list of banned weapons (nor did he include herbicides). Napalm and gases, then, are still included in our arsenal of weapons for waging limited wars.

One of the most destructive tactics that U. S. forces have developed for usage in Vietnam is the pattern bombing by B-52's. Originally strategic bombers carrying nuclear weapons, the B-52's have been adapted for delivery of conventional loads. The purpose of pattern bombing was summarized as follows in 1965 by the U. S. mission in Saigon:

. . . a spoiling mission designed to harass the enemy and to disrupt his operations, facilities and morals. The B-52s were used because of their unique ability to place heavy concentrations of bombs over a wide area. They are especially useful in jungle areas where specific targets cannot be pinpointed for tactical bombing because of the heavy tree canopy.[9]

B-52s are used for military purposes against enemy troop concentrations and to deny them access to certain areas. Furthermore, B-52 bombing is an extremely effective psychological weapon. There is no

8. Jack Raymond, "Gas as a Weapon," *Army*, May, 1965.
9. Quoted in Jack Langguth, *New York Times*, July 5, 1966.

warning of a B-52 attack; the bombers fly in un-
molested by groundfire or missiles from Guam or
Thailand and drop their bombs from 20,000 feet. On
the ground the planes cannot be heard and there is
no indication that there is a bombing run in progress
until the bombs explode. After delivering their bomb-
loads in South Vietnam, the B-52 pilots fly back to
their safe posts in Guam or Thailand.

Frank Harvey, in *Air War: Vietnam,* describes the
mission of B-52 raids:

> To blast or burn large areas of jungle (also
> roads, buildings and fields) containing living
> things, animals and men, some innocent and
> unaware, without warning.[10]

The bombing is indiscriminate and is destroying and
pockmarking the countryside of South Vietnam. It is
largely because of the loads that these planes carry
that the statistics of our bombing in Vietnam are so
fantastic. Each B-52 is capable of carrying fifty 750
pound bombs.[11]

Recently, they have been dropping 10,000 pound
demolition bombs. Since 1965, U. S. planes have
dropped over 4½ million tons of bombs on North
and South Vietnam.[12]

10. *Air War: Vietnam,* p. 127.
11. "Changing the Rules of Guerrilla War," *Business Week,*
March 5, 1966.
12. Professor Gabriel Kolko, history professor at the State
University of New York at Buffalo, at the Congressional Conference on War and National Responsibility; and Len Ackland,
"The New Isolationism . . . ," *The Peace Times,* March 7,
1970, and the Public Affairs Office of the Pentagon.

This means that we have dropped about 300 pounds of explosives for every citizen in North and South Vietnam, over 36 tons of bombs for every square mile of land in both Vietnams (calculated and updated from estimates in the *New York Post*, December 5, 1967). The tonnage has long surpassed that dropped during World War II.

Another weapon being used extensively in Vietnam is the M-16 rifle. It was developed in the early 1960s and field tested in Vietnam. John S. Tompkins described its initial history in Vietnam:

It fast became the most sought-after piece of equipment among our advisors and Vietnamese soldiers. Stories began to filter back about the lethality (a military euphemism for killing power) of the new rifle. Though the bullet was only a third as heavy as that fired by our service rifle, it hit with such velocity that it seemed to explode the target rather than punch a hole through it. The shock seemed so great that most of the Vietcong hit died even from what would normally have been superficial wounds.[13]

The M-16 is now the standard rifle carried by U. S. troops in Vietnam.

13. Tompkins, *The Weapons of World War III*, p. 123.

Bibliography

Len Ackland, "The New Isolationism . . . ," *The Peace Times*, March 7, 1970.

Annual Reports of Publically-Held Companies

Aviation Week and Space Technology, "Bomb Dispensers Help USAF Match Ordnance Targets," December 11, 1967, p. 79.

———, "Limited War Weapons Tested at Elgin AFB," Mid-December, 1966, pp. 36ff.

William Beecher, "Way-Out Weapons," *The New York Times Sunday Magazine*, March 24, 1968, pp. 49ff.

Cecil Brownlow, "Limited War Problems Challenge Industry," *Aviation Week and Space Technology*, March 14, 1966, p. 26.

———, "USAF Boosts North Viet ECM Jamming," *Aviation Week and Space Technology*, February 2, 1967, p. 23.

Business Week, "Changing the Rules of Guerilla War," March 5, 1966.

Clergy and Laymen Concerned About the War, *In the Name of America*.

Congressional Conference on War and National Responsibility, February 20 and 21, 1970.

Robert Crichton, "Our Air War," *The New York Review of Books*, January 4, 1968, p. 3.

DMS Market Intelligence Report, Ordnance Volume. (A McGraw-Hill Publication).

Defense Supply Agency, *The Defense Industry Bulletin.*

Department of the Army, *Rockets,* February, 1958.

Department of the Army, *Land Mines,* 1964.

Departments of the Army and the Air Force, *Chemical Bombs and Clusters,* May, 1957.

Departments of the Army, Air Force, and the Navy, *Bombs and Bomb Components,* April, 1966.

Department of Defense, "100 Companies Listed According to Value of Military Prime Contracts," Fiscal Years 1968 and 1969.

Forbes, "Back for More," April 1, 1968.

Foreign Trade and Tariff Proposals, Hearings Before the House Ways and Means Committee, June-July, 1968.

Frank Harvey, *Air War: Vietnam,* Bantam Books, New York, 1967.

Jewel Substitutes in Watch Movements, Hearings Before the House Ways and Means Committee, July 27-28, 1968.

Lee Lockwood, "Recollections of Four Weeks with the Enemy," *Life,* April 7, 1967.

Moody's *Industrial Manual,* 1969.

The Nation, "Good Americans," July 8, 1968.

National Action/Research on the Military Industrial Complex, *Weapons for Counterinsurgency,* American Friends Service Committee, Philadelphia, 1970.

Ordnance, September-October, 1966, p. 144.
   March-April, 1967, p. 482.
   May-June, 1968, p. 532.

C. M. Plattner, "Limited-War Concepts Weighed in Battle," *Aviation Week and Space Technology,*" January 31, 1966, p. 42.

———, "Marine Control of Air Tested in Combat," *Aviation Week and Space Technology,* February 14, 1966, pp. 90ff.

Poor's *Guide to Corporations* 1970.

Eric Prokosch, "'Conventional' Killers," *The New Republic,* November 1, 1969.

———, "The Vietnam Profiteers."

Jack Raymond, "Gas As A Weapon," *Army,* May, 1965.

Jean-Paul Sartre and Arlette El Kaim-Sartre, *On Genocide and a Summary of the Evidence and the Judgments of the International War Crimes Tribunal,* Beacon Press, Boston, 1968.

Jonathan Schell, *The Military Half,* Vintage Books, New York, 1968.

———, *The Village of Ben Suc,* Vintage Books, New York, 1968.

U.S. Grant Sharp and William Westmoreland, *Report on the War in Vietnam,* U.S. Government Printing Office, Washington, D.C., 1968.

Standard & Poor's Surveys, 1967, 1968, 1969.

The Stockholm International Peace Research Institute, *SIPRI Yearbook of World Armaments and Disarmament, 1968/69,* Almquist & Wicksell, Stockholm; Humanities Press, New York; and Gerald Duckworth & Co., Ltd., London; 1969.

John S. Tompkins, *The Weapons of World War III,* Doubleday, Garden City, New York, 1966.

Wall Street Transcript, June 17, 1968.

Washington Post, "Nine Australians Killed by Own Mines," March 2, 1970.

Thomas Whiteside, "Reporter at Large," *The New Yorker,* February 2, 1970.

Who's Who in America 1968-1969.

Index

This index is a listing of
products and manufacturers only.

70 71 72 73   12 11 10 9 8 7 6 5 4 3 2 1

Council on Economic Priorities—Annual Subscriptions
(Check box—Tear out sheet)

	ECONOMIC PRIORITIES REPORTS	ECONOMIC PRIORITIES REPORTS & IN-DEPTH STUDIES
☐ Supporting Member	$25	$40
☐ Sustaining Member	$100	$150
☐ Corporate/Institutional	$250	$350
☐ Donors ($500 or more) Please indicate number of publications requested.	$—	$—
☐ Single copy of In-Depth Study on Pollution and the Paper-Pulping Industry		$10

| ☐ Special Subscription Rate for Students and Clergy. | $5 | $10 |

Council on Economic Priorities
1028 Connecticut Ave. • Washington, D.C. 20036
(202) 466–2250 • (202) 296–5550   Ext. 926
New York City (212) 248–3737

Name _____   Affiliation _____

Street _____   City _____

State _____   Zip Code _____